Christy was determined not to marry the man her grandfather had chosen for her. This was the twentieth century, she wouldn't be bullied. In her determination to jump out of the frying pan, would she land in the fire?

THE ONLY CHARITY

BY

SARA SEALE

MILLS & BOON LIMITED
17–19 FOLEY STREET
LONDON W1A 1DR

*All the characters in this book have no existence outside
the imagination of the Author, and have no relation
whatsoever to anyone bearing the same name or names.
They are not even distantly inspired by any individual
known or unknown to the Author, and all the incidents
are pure invention.*

First published 1961

This edition 1973

© Sara Seale 1961

*For copyright reasons, this book may not be issued on loan
or otherwise except in its original soft cover*

ISBN 0 263 71481 0

*Made and Printed in Great Britain by
Richard Clay (The Chaucer Press), Ltd., Bungay, Suffolk*

CHAPTER ONE

SHE sat with her tall, barely touched glass of lemon shandy outside the little inn, frowning at the gently foaming water which lapped against the sea-wall and thinking of that final scene with her grandfather. The sunlight and the cries of the gulls were a familiar pattern to the mornings, as was the friendly rise and fall of voices from the tap-room. No one ever bothered her, for they all knew her; the fishermen gave her a passing salutation and sometimes a yachtsman, new to those parts, would cast a speculative eye upon her, to be gently called to order by the landlord; but it was not very often that she came to the inn, except to inquire about boats for hire or, as now, to sort out a problem and while away an idle hour.

'Idle hours!' the old man had stormed, when she had tried to explain the urge which had made her rent a cottage in this remote Cornish village in order to paint, even though she knew she had little talent. 'What do you want with idle hours at your age, my girl? You should marry and settle down.'

'Not that old chestnut all over again,' she had said, trying to make fun of it. 'When I marry, the man will be of my choice, not yours, Gramp. Besides, how do you know my affections aren't already engaged?'

The tilt of disdain to her absurd nose was both familiar and endearing to him. Just so had her mother looked when defying him, before they had finally quarrelled.

'The first young blackguard who'll snap you up for your expectations? Oh no, Christy. Your mother made that mistake over her second marriage. I'll not have my granddaughter doing the same. You'll marry the man I've chosen and make the best of it.'

'Really!' she exclaimed, exasperated. 'You're making an absolute *thing* about this—advertising all over the place for remote family connections and finding only one eligible in the wilds of Northumberland or somewhere. How do you know he isn't married already?'

'I've checked.'

'Darling, you *are* absurd!' He was not to be taken seriously, of course, but this particular foible was becoming a little irritating. 'You've no reason to suppose a perfect stranger would be willing to dance to your piping, even if I would.'

'Folks will do most things for money, and you're not a bad-looking wench,' he replied with a grin.

'Well, *I* wouldn't. I don't want your money. I've got some of my own,' she retorted, as she often had before.

'But you want Fairmile, don't you?' he replied with gentle slyness, and her narrow face set in the stubborn lines with which he was becoming familiar.

'Fairmile is my inheritance,' she said proudly. 'I'm the last of the Taveners, after all. Even though I'm the wrong sex, you surely wouldn't leave the place to strangers?'

'I'll leave my property where I choose,' he snapped, enjoying her discomfiture. 'But we might strike a bargain, you and I. You wouldn't want the place to go to strangers, would you, now?'

He had, as usual, put an unerring finger on her one weakness. Fairmile ... that gracious house which she had known as a child but which in adolescence her mother had cheated her out of ... calling home.... How cruel the old man was to dangle it as bait to satisfy his own selfish desires. The place should, as her right, come to her.

Then she looked at him and, as so often before, warmed towards him. He was no more selfish than other rich men who could crack the whip at will, merely stubborn and quite unable to understand why he should not get his own way; in that, she supposed, they had something in common.

6

'You can't,' she said, the thought uppermost in her mind, 'blame me for inheriting your pigheadedness, Gramp. I'll not, any more than my mother did, regulate my life to suit you. We've been strangers too long and this isn't an age any more where a suitable arranged marriage cuts any ice—besides, you know nothing about me. I may already be committed.'

'Strangers, yes,' he said, and sighed deeply, ignoring the hint which she had thrown out. 'Your mother took you from me, bringing you up in foreign places, away from your birthright, and stuffing you with independent notions quite unsuitable to a female.'

'My mother took me away because you wouldn't accept her new husband, as you well know,' she told him coolly. 'She, too, had inherited some of your pigheadedness. It wasn't until they were both killed in that plane crash that you thought of getting in touch. If I'd been a boy you would have been clamouring for me long ago.'

He glanced at her shyly under his shaggy brows. She was not built like the women he had admired in his youth, but he could appreciate the slender lines of her young body, despite that hideous modern disguise known as jeans and the accompanying pony-tail. She was flaxen-fair, like her mother, with the same surprisingly black eyebrows and, if she could not lay claim to the same beauty, she still had the Tavener hallmark and a quality which might, perhaps, prove more dangerous than mere beauty. She had, despite their quarrels, become very dear to him, and only rarely did he admit to himself that they were indeed strangers and he knew little or nothing of her private life. Well, she could be coerced, like all the others.

'Ah, Christy, youth can be very cruel. What have I to live for now?' he said, looking, for a moment, the picture of defeated old age. His granddaughter turned to look at him, her eyes softening as they took in afresh the familiar wheelchair, the slumped figure which had once been strong and

7

massive, the bearded face, still ruddy, but creased and puckered with sickness, or it could have been over-indulgence in his youth.

'Gramp . . .' she said softly, stretching her narrow hands towards him in a small gesture of an unconscious charm, then she caught the unholy glint in the eyes which were still so bright and youthful, and stamped her foot at him.

'You're an absolute old fraud!' she cried. 'You ought to be ashamed of yourself, trying to get round me with phoney pathos! If you think I'll agree to marry this wretched kinsman of ours just because you like to believe you're helpless and must be humoured, then you've picked the wrong girl. I'll not marry a man I've never seen for you or anybody else. Why should I?'

'But you might for Fairmile, eh?'

'Not even for Fairmile,' she said, but she turned almost unconsciously to the window to gaze across those pleasant acres; to the stately mile of chestnut-lined avenue which gave the place its name; to the glancing evening sunlight of an English summer's day breaking through the trees, and knew again that strange nostalgia for this place she had known long, long ago in childhood, and had scarcely remembered. She had enjoyed to the full her unconventional upbringing, the freedom and perpetual change of foreign domiciles, but Fairmile had always been home, the place where one day she would lay her bones, even though it should only be in the family vault.

Sir Harry Tavener watched her for a time in silence. Sometimes he knew instinctively that words unspoken would serve his ends best, but this was not one of them.

'I'd advise you not to dally too long, my girl,' he said with a chuckle. 'Brown has a mind to marry me, crippled though I am, and I might oblige her yet. You wouldn't like my nurse-companion queening it here after I'm gone, would you?'

She swung round from the window, the long fair tail of

hair flying out behind her.

'Brown!' she exclaimed incredulously. 'You must be dreaming, Gramp! Brown's a nice, quiet, negative little thing who probably gave up thinking of marriage long ago.'

'And that's the insufferable conceit of youth,' he said with a certain grim enjoyment. 'What do you know of Brown and her kind, Miss Disdain? Has she no dreams and ambitions because she's turned thirty and keeps in the background?'

'I—I didn't mean to be disparaging,' Christy replied, sounding a little bewildered. 'It's just that I've never thought of Brown like that. She's been a wonderful nurse and companion for you and I hope you'll reward her suitably in your will, but I think you're flattering yourself a little if you imagine she's setting her cap at you.'

'I don't flatter myself, m'dear,' he retorted dryly. 'I have plenty to offer in the way of this world's goods, and it wouldn't be the first time an elderly patient married his nurse.'

'You're just trying to rile me into getting your own way. You wouldn't marry Brown and leave no descendants to inherit Fairmile.'

'What do you know about such things? I'm not in my dotage yet and my legs will carry me when I choose.'

'Then why don't you choose more often, instead of making people push you about all over the place in a chair?' she retaliated with childish rudeness, and at once they became plunged into one of their violent quarrels.

As so often happened the subject that had sparked the matter off became lost or forgotten, so that when Rose Brown came quietly into the room wheeling the trolley which bore the pre-dinner drinks, Christy felt no embarrassment or, indeed, any curiosity. She was merely relieved that the rather disgraceful shouting-match should be broken up.

'For heaven's sake, do your stuff and soothe the savage

breast,' she said, lighting a cigarette and perching on the window-seat to gaze out again on the evening light.

'Now, Sir Harry, you really shouldn't get so excited,' Brown said, her voice cool and slightly amused as she began to mix the drinks.

'Excited—I'm nothing of the sort!' Sir Harry hit back. 'It's this girl here you should take to task, if you want me calm, my good woman. She does my blood pressure no good—no good at all.'

'I dare say she had provocation,' Brown said with a faint smile, and Christy turned to throw her an answering smile.

Dear Brown, she thought, how cool, how impartial; how utterly ridiculous of Gramp to trail her as such a blatant red herring.

'He's back on the old long-playing record,' she said lightly. 'Can't you make him understand, Brown, that in these days girls aren't married off high-handedly without due reference to their likes and dislikes?'

'Stuff and nonsense! Who's trying to force you into anything, you addle-pated creature?' muttered Sir Harry; but Rose Brown, ignoring the interruption, said gravely:

'Perhaps you should think further than the present, Christy. With youth, and a little money, life can be very sweet, but there comes a time—but perhaps for you it won't.'

Christy stared at her, seeing her for possibly the first time as a woman with dreams and a private life of her own. One did not, she supposed uncomfortably, give enough thought to people in one's employ. Brown had been Brown, cool and efficient, appearing negative, perhaps, because she was disciplined. She was like her name, Christy thought, a study in sepia with muted, if few, highlights, but the large brown eyes were full and clear, the soft brown hair constrained to a neatness which denied its natural wave, and the good lines of her tall figure were suitably subdued by the stiff, familiar overalls she wore.

'Why don't you loosen up, Brownie?' Christy asked curiously.

'Loosen up?'

'Get rid of the overalls and prim hair-do. I'm sure my grandfather would much prefer to have something frivolous around, wouldn't you, Gramp?'

Sir Harry's bushy eyebrows lifted in innocent surprise, but his keen old eyes were twinkling as they travelled from his granddaughter to his nurse.

'What's this?' he asked with sudden mildness. 'An exchange of feminine advice? Brown's all right as she is. At least she doesn't screw her hair up into a ridiculous pony-tail or wear the pants that would only have been seen on a navvy in my young day.'

'I'm a little old for jeans and pony-tails, Sir Harry,' Brown said demurely, but there was a fleeting quirk to her lips that made Christy think uncomfortably that she might be laughing at them both.

'Rubbish!' she said a little impatiently. 'You may not be the type for jeans, Brown, but I've seen you on your days out when you become human and feminine and definitely attractive.'

'But that hasn't really occurred to you until now, has it?' Brown said gently, and Christy frowned, and fell silent.

No, she acknowledged uneasily to herself, it had not really occurred to her. Her own visits to Fairmile in the past year had been intermittent and of brief duration, and she had been too busy charming or quarrelling with her grandfather to have more than a passing interest in his nurse. It was odd that she should remember now the way Brown had looked with her hair loose and the unfamiliar femininity of a swirling skirt or a bright touch of lipstick.

'Do we take you for granted?' she asked a little humbly, and was aware that the lashes which suddenly veiled the nurse's eyes were long and silky and somehow secretive.

'You take me as you should, Christy—as a piece of your

11

background,' Brown replied tranquilly. 'Are you ready for another drink?'

Christy accepted the glass of sherry but left it almost untouched on the window-seat beside her and gazed moodily about the gracious, but shabby, room, aware that to Brown's thirty-odd years, her own untried twenty, combined with independence and no necessity to work, must seem something of a small affront. It would appear an unfair distribution of this world's blessings, she thought, and wondered whether she should be enjoying her freedom so much. She could, she knew, make a permanent home with her grandfather, but she was restless and wanted to find her feet before settling down, whether it should be to marriage or the dutiful obligations of a granddaughter awaiting her inheritance; besides which, there was no guarantee, for all his affection, that Sir Harry would make his will in her favour should she not indulge whatever whim he might have at the moment, and for the present his whim appeared to be the very irksome one of marrying her off to some remote kinsman neither of them knew.

'Well?' he suddenly barked, making her jump. 'You're not going to grace my table in those outrageous garments, are you? It's a bare half-hour to dinner-time.'

She got to her feet, ruffled his thick shock of white hair with affectionate impertinence as she passed his chair and said impulsively to Brown:

'Come with me and help me change. We can have a girlish natter.'

The nurse looked surprised, but glancing inquiringly at her patient, found him grinning with faint malice.

'Go on,' he jeered. 'You might as well add lady's maid to your other duties. My granddaughter, as you can judge for yourself, inherits her share of the Tavener exigence. Put the trolley at my elbow so that I can help myself in your absence.'

'Speak for yourself,' Christy retorted, making a face at

12

him. '*I* don't want to make use of Brownie. I simply want her company.'

They went up the wide staircase together, Christy's hand lingering lovingly on the polished rail.

'It's a beautiful staircase, isn't it?' she said, pausing to admire the smooth marble steps, the delicate scrolling of the wrought-iron balustrade.

'Yes, beautiful,' Brown replied a little shortly. 'But Fairmile is a beautiful house, run to seed.'

Christy tucked a hand through the nurse's arm.

'Run to seed? Yes, I suppose so. Brownie—you didn't really think I just wanted you to do lady's maid, did you? It was just Gramp's rather crude idea of a joke, you know,' she said, and thought she felt the other woman withdraw a little, but when she spoke her voice was as tranquil as usual.

'I ought to know my patient by now,' she answered. 'But you shouldn't excite him too much, Christy. He may enjoy these wrangles and arguments, but they aren't good for him.'

'I know he's practically lost the use of his legs through arthritis, and his blood pressure's high, his arteries hardening or something, but he's strong as an ox, I should think.' Christy's voice was still light, but the nurse spoke more gravely.

'You haven't much medical knowledge, my dear. His heart is none too sound,' she said, and Christy remembered her grandfather saying not so long ago: 'Youth can be very cruel ... what have I to live for now?'

'What are you trying to tell me?' she asked in alarm. 'Gramp loves to pull out the tremolo stop if he thinks he can get round you. There's nothing in it, surely?'

They had turned the corner of the long gallery which led off from the staircase, and Christy had stopped dead. The house seemed suddenly very quiet, very aloof; too big for one old man who might be nearing the end of his time, too big and too empty to welcome the next generation unless there was promise of others to come.

'You frighten me, Brownie,' Christy said, and indeed she looked frightened, dwelling for a brief instant on a suspended measure of time.

Brown's voice came, cool and prosaic.

'I don't mean to frighten you, my dear, but one must face possible contingencies. I'm only trying to warn you not to thwart him too obviously.'

'You mean I ought to agree to this ridiculous notion of marrying me off to some seedy connection simply because he bears the name of Tavener?'

'Oh well, as to that I wouldn't know, but it does no harm to compromise, does it? These moods pass. Come along to your room and get out of those jeans or we'll be late for dinner, and that won't be so popular.'

They went into Christy's room, its faded tapestries and mellowed furniture bathed in the late sunlight which flooded in from the west window. Christy rummaged in the great armoire which served as a wardrobe, flinging garments on to the bed.

'What shall I wear?' she asked. 'What do you think he'd like?'

'The white crêpe. It's so feminine and virginal and unsophisticated,' Brown replied, and Christy thought she detected an undercurrent of mockery in her reply.

'That's all you know,' she replied a little shortly. 'It isn't unsophisticated at all—just clever.'

'But then,' said Brown, with smiling apology, 'I wouldn't know about the sort of clothes you can afford. The dress just seems to me a simple little thing.'

'Brown—what did you mean when you said it did no harm to compromise?' Christy asked, beginning to brush out her hair.

'What I said, I suppose. You could humour the old man instead of opposing him—Get changed, for heaven's sake!'

14

Obediently the girl put down her brush and started scrambling into fresh underclothes, tearing shoulder straps in her haste, swearing mildly and rather absurdly, with a mischievous eye on the nurse for a possible reaction.

'It doesn't occur to either of you, I suppose, that my affections might already be engaged?' she said casually.

Brown looked faintly amused.

'Naturally it's occurred to me,' she replied. 'You're attractive and not exactly penniless. Is there someone, then, or shouldn't I ask?'

'I have dozens of admirers,' Christy said in the casual tone of voice that she might have announced that she had dozens of pairs of tights. 'Girls with comfortable incomes aren't easily come by these days.'

'No, I imagine not. Anyone special?'

'That would be telling,' said Christy, with her wide grin. She did not imagine Brown's questions were any more serious than her own answers, but the nurse gave her a swift look from under her lashes.

'Thinking of producing a decoy duck, were you?' she asked.

'A decoy duck? What do you mean?'

'Well, a *fait accompli* might put a stopper on the seedy connection, as you call him, mightn't it?'

'It's an idea,' said Christy thoughtfully, her eyes beginning to dance, then she paused. There was a flaw in it somewhere and almost at once she saw it.

'If I did that he'd most likely cut me out of his will for sheer spite,' she said.

Brown asked softly:

'And would you really mind, except for Fairmile? After all, you have money of your own.'

'I don't mind a row of beans about his money, but Fairmile—well, you see, to me Fairmile's always been a kind of touchstone. I feel I belong here. Besides, it's my right, isn't it?'

15

'Then you might effect another compromise. The house for you and the money to—whoever else Sir Harry has in mind,' said Brown lightly, and Christy gave her a curious glance, remembering her grandfather's outrageous boast earlier in the evening. Was it possible that quiet, efficient and usually self-effacing Brown really had hopes of marrying her patient? Well, good luck to her, thought Christy blithely, if it was only the money she was after. It might be quite amusing to have a stepgrandmother not much more than ten years older than oneself.

'You think of the quaintest things,' she said, dismissing the whole absurd suggestion from her mind. 'Be a dear and hook me up, will you?'

The last hook fastened, she dashed back to the dressing-table, and began to make up her face with her usual careless hurry. She caught sight of the nurse's expression in the glass and turned swiftly on the stool.

'Brown—you didn't really think what Gramp said was true, did you? About using you as a lady's maid, I mean?'

'You've asked me that already,' Brown replied with a hint of irritability. Christy suddenly annoyed her. Sitting on the stool in her white dress with her hair falling over her face, she looked like a little girl; the sort of little girl who, all her life, had been shielded from hard facts and demanded tolerance and liking as her right.

'Have I?' Christy sounded humble. 'It's only that—well, I—I wouldn't like your feelings to be hurt inadvertently, dear Brownie. I'm very fond of you.'

'Are you, Christy?' Brown sounded abstracted.

She was, in fact, trying to assess the girl's attraction. Not beautiful by any stretch of imagination, she thought, scarcely even pretty, though the colouring was arresting— that hair and those black eyebrows over eyes that were a bright clear hazel when they should have been blue. Then the tanned, rather narrow face lit up with that wide, in- genuous smile which was essentially Christy's, and Brown

16

had to smile in return, despite her own reservations.

'We seem to have been talking a great deal of nonsense. Will you be staying long this time?' she said.

Christy turned back to the dressing-table, aware that the nurse was putting up barriers. She had been quite genuine in her profession of liking for Brown, but it was not very comfortable to be made subtly aware that the liking might not be returned.

'Not very long,' she said. 'The summer's nearly over and my lease of the cottage will be up.'

'Will you come back here, then?'

'Perhaps. It rather depends on what bee in his bonnet Gramp happens to have at that time. I expect I shall end by going back to the London flat. The two girls are always anxious to welcome me as a p.g.'

'Finding out already that money opens most doors?' Brown asked, and Christy scowled suddenly at their twin reflections in the glass.

'Naturally one expects to pay one's way,' she replied with sudden coolness. 'Liz and Cara aren't well off and my contribution helps with the rent. Besides, I wouldn't like it any other way.'

Brown got up and began to collect the garments so carelessly scattered on the bed and put them away.

'Naturally—I wasn't criticizing,' she said. 'I only sometimes wonder why you prefer to racket around instead of settling here, where you say you belong.'

'Racket around?' Christy repeated, her dark eyebrows lifting in surprise. 'Is that how you see my life? I haven't been living in this country much more than a year and I've been finding my feet. We don't live a wildly gay life in the London flat, you know. The girls work, and when I'm there I keep house for them, and paint a bit in my spare time. I also attend art school for the good of my soul. Why should I settle down here at the crack of Gramp's whip when all these years he's done nothing for me because I wasn't a

17

boy? He understands that very well.'

'Does he? I've never understood.'

'But you must know the old story, Brown. Gramp wanted sons—rows of stalwart Taveners to carry on the traditions of his youth and produce more sons, and all he got was a solitary daughter. When she married he made my father change his name to Tavener, hoping for grandsons, but all he got was me. Then when my father died and Mother married again he thought he could work the same trick and there was still time for a grandson, but my step-father was quite a different kettle of fish. He wouldn't change his name for a start, neither would he settle in England, even with Fairmile dangled as bait. He and my mother were very happy, but there were no sons—no more children at all.'

Brown glanced at the girl curiously. Had there been bitterness in that little speech or simply amusement that such old-fashioned schemes had failed to come to fruition?

'You mind, Christy?' she asked, tentatively.

'Not particularly. If I'd been a boy, Gramp would have raised heaven and earth to get me back long ago. It wasn't until I came and looked him up myself that he had second thoughts, but he can't dictate and he knows it—I'm independent financially, thanks to my parents. I am, of course, his last hope for male heirs, but living abroad so much hasn't conditioned me to an out-dated feudal system.'

How sure she was, thought the nurse with sudden bitterness, how insulated in her financial independence, how much an echo of that feudal system which she saw fit to laugh at.

'Don't you care at all about Sir Harry?' she asked with sudden sharpness, and the girl swung back again from the mirror, her thin little face alight with affection and that wide smile which could never be associated with rancour.

'But I adore him—I thought you knew that,' she exclaimed. 'It's only that I'm not going to be pushed around

18

because I don't happen to be a grandson, and Gramp must understand that by now. Say what you will, Brown, he respects my independence. I don't think he'd have me otherwise, despite his disappointment in my sex.'

'He's besotted about you,' the nurse said with a sudden bite to her voice, and Christy's smile became uncertain.

'You said that as though you resented it,' she said slowly, aware again that this quiet, usually reserved woman had private opinions which might not always be pleasant to hear.

Brown turned to look at her, and her face was once more the familiar, pleasant mask, disciplined to hide emotion, schooled to please the providers of her bread and butter.

'Why should I resent such a natural phenomenon?' she inquired pleasantly. 'You're very attractive, Christy, and Sir Harry, for all this rather ridiculous talk of grandsons, hasn't lost his eye for a pretty woman, I don't mind betting.'

'He used to be a terror in his palmy days, so I believe,' Christy said, the grin returning. 'Poor Gramp—he must have been very lonely when all his schemes went wrong.'

'Loneliness isn't a thing the young can readily understand—nor should they,' Brown said.

'Are you lonely, sometimes?' Christy asked softly, and for a moment the older woman's lips tightened.

'Oh yes,' she said lightly. 'I've never married, you see, and it *is* lonely living in other people's houses.'

'Yes, I can imagine so. But you've been happy here, haven't you, Brownie? Gramp depends a great deal on you, I know.'

'Oh yes, I've been happy. If one must have a home at second-hand, Fairmile couldn't be bettered.'

'No, it couldn't, could it? A home at second-hand ... perhaps that's all either of us has got ...'

'*You!*' the nurse's voice was suddenly sharp and bitter. 'You can take what you want with a flick of a finger if you aren't too pigheaded to know how! There's the dinner-gong. I must go and get out of my overall.'

Christy sat where she was for a few moments longer, her uncertainty returning. She could not remember having talked so intimately to the nurse before, nor was she sure that she liked the trend their conversation had taken.

The sun was sinking now behind the great spreading trees of the chestnut avenue, leaving a chill behind. She gave a little shiver, feeling the cool air on her bare neck and arms, and jumped up swiftly to run down to the familiar warmth of her grandfather's presence and the excellent dinner which she knew would await them.

She never knew quite what had precipitated the final scene between them, and her own headlong plunge into preposterous fantasy. Perhaps her assurance had been shaken by the brief glimpses Brown had shown her of another point of view, perhaps the joke of the old man's absurd plans for her had gone sour and, in the end, perhaps it was simply possible that the nurse's idle suggestion of counter-attack had taken root and borne fruit. She only remembered that after Brown had tactfully withdrawn, when dinner was over, to leave them to a pleasant evening, they were suddenly shouting at each other.

Like all old bones of contention the validity of the subject had ceased to exist, and they hurled abuse at one another. Sir Harry went through the formidable range of his repertoire, sarcasm turning to pathos, pathos to rage, but he could not move her. She was not afraid of him as her mother had been and she possessed his own gift for stubborn refusal to compromise and of burning her boats on the grand scale, which she now proceeded to do.

'It's no good trying to persuade me any more,' she stormed at him. 'I couldn't marry your beastly candidate, even supposing he was willing, which I don't suppose for a moment he is, since he hasn't been consulted. I'm not free.'

'What in hell do you mean?'

'What I say. What do you know about me as a person? Why shouldn't it have occurred to you that I might already have plans of my own?'

'What plans could a chit of your age have that could interfere with mine?'

'The most natural of all. I'm married already,' she flung back at him, and knew as she spoke that the preposterous lie had only that moment popped into her head.

For a moment he looked dumbfounded. Then he roared:

'Stuff and nonsense! How could you get married without my sanction?'

'Very easily. I'm well over the age of consent and since you've refused to have anything to do with me until a year ago you can hardly expect to rank as parent or guardian,' she retorted, enjoying for the instant that small victory over him.

'I don't believe it!' he blustered, but he began to sound uncertain. Wasn't it the sort of stupidity that someone with his own hot blood in their veins might well have perpetrated?

She was too angry to think of retracting, too astonished at the simplicity with which an intolerable situation could be ended. Produce a decoy duck, Brown had said. Well, she would do better than that, she would invent an imaginary husband, a very final answer to this importunate grandparent.

'Are you foxing me by any chance?' he asked, his beard beginning to quiver, and for a moment she hesitated. No; tell a lie and stick to it was the golden rule. If she threw away the prospect of Fairmile into the bargain, then it couldn't be helped. At least it would put an end to this ridiculous situation which had now grown out of all proportion and sunk to the absurdity of Victorian melodrama.

'No,' she said, and he struggled for a moment in his wheelchair as if he would rise to his feet, then sank back again, his face puffed and choleric.

'I don't believe it,' he said, then shot her a quick, suspicious look. 'That cottage in Cornwall—I always did think that was an unnatural way for a young girl to spend the summer—alone, painting unsaleable daubs. *Painting!* So you weren't alone, then? You were honeymooning with some long-haired artist feller after your money.'

She was silent from sheer surprise at the ease with which he had suddenly accepted the story, but she supposed that to his type of masculine mind this explanation of the cottage was easier to understand than the real one.

'You damned little fool!' he shouted savagely. 'Hadn't you the sense to bring your prospective suitor here first? I'd have soon sized him up and sent him packing!'

'My life is my own affair. I owe you nothing, Gramp,' she retaliated hotly. 'You disowned us all those years, my mother and I, and now you think you can push me around because you're old and, perhaps, a little sorry, and hang out Fairmile as bait.'

'Sorry, am I? That's where you're wrong, my girl, and as for Fairmile—you'll not get the place now to pass on to any brats you and that no-good feller may have.'

'I thought that's what you wanted, brats—grandsons to make up for the sons you never had.'

'I want Tavener brats, carrying the same name. Oh, no, my fine lady, you've spiked your own guns there. You should have played your hand with more finesse if you wanted to get round me on that score.'

'I've not been trying to get round you,' she said, looking suddenly like her mother, cool and proud and disdainful. 'I've made no secret of the fact that I hoped one day Fairmile would come to me, but I wasn't going to bargain with you. I won't sell my independence for a—for a mess of pottage.'

He snorted rudely.

'Mess of pottage, indeed! Fine words, fine words, m'dear, but they'll get you nowhere. Go back to this good-for-nothing husband of yours and enjoy your so-called independence. You'll get nothing more from me.'

'Don't you want to know where I met him—how—how long I've—I've been married?' she asked curiously, beginning to realize the significance of her rash statement. He banged a clenched fist down on the arm of his chair.

'What should I care? You're ashamed of him, obviously, or you'd have brought him here to Fairmile.'

'I'm ashamed of nothing and nobody—except you, sometimes, when I remember how you treated my mother.'

'Get out, get out!' he shouted. 'I've finished with the lot of you—and don't come running back here when you find out your mistake, for I've no use for humble pie.'

'And you'll not get it!' she shouted back, now as angry as he, and at the same moment, Tom, the old manservant who had been in Sir Harry's service for years, came into the room, looking shocked and anxious.

'Sir Harry! Miss Christy! They can hear you all over the house,' he quavered. 'It's not good for your heart, sir, to fly into these passions. Miss Christy, you should know better.'

'I'm in a passion, too, Tom,' she cried, stamping her foot at him. 'A great big whale of a passion, fit to burn you up and everyone else, too. I'm leaving in the morning, so will you ask Noakes to have my car filled up and bring it round first thing?'

'Leaving, miss?'

'Yes, leaving—back to a husband she didn't see fit to tell any of us about, and good riddance,' said Sir Harry, his eyes beginning to bulge.

'Husband? Deary me ... I'd best fetch Miss Brown...'

'Yes, fetch her, and stop repeating everything we say. Go on, get out—and you, too, Christy! I've finished with you.'

Christy went, with a flutter of white skirts and flying hair, and, after that, the house seemed to echo for a long time with raised voices and running feet.

'He's had a slight heart attack,' Brown said, looking in on Christy much later, and the girl sat up in her great four-poster, lifting a face already marked with weeping, in swift alarm.

'Should I go to him, Brown? It's—it's all my fault, I'm afraid,' she said, but found no answering reassurance in the nurse's expression. The earlier intimacy between them had vanished, or perhaps it had never been. In the shadows of the lamp-lit room, Brown's face was cold and clinical.

'No, he doesn't want to see you,' she said. 'Did you have to go so far, Christy?'

'What do you mean? It was your idea to produce a counterblast. I can explain in the morning.'

'Can you? I should leave things as they are, my dear. After all, you've made your point, haven't you?'

Christy blinked in the light.

'But, Brown, you said——' she began a little helplessly, and the nurse smiled, as one would at a wayward child who had been sent to bed in disgrace.

'If you're referring to our conversation before dinner, I was talking idly, as I imagined you understood,' she said. 'After all, I wasn't to know the ins and outs of your private life. You could have come clean about this in the first place and saved us all a lot of trouble.'

'But, Brown, you don't *believe*——'

'That you're already married? Why not? As you told me earlier, you had plenty of admirers. It would only be natural, I imagine, to keep your marriage secret until you saw which way the wind blew with your grandfather.'

Christy stared at her. The stormy interview, the absurd falsehoods, had already dwindled to a sense of absurdity and shame; it was inconceivable that Brown who had, perhaps unwittingly, inspired the whole thing, should refuse to co-operate.

'I don't understand,' she muttered, pushing the hair out of her eyes. 'What have you to gain from wanting me to

24

stick to my story?'

'Only my patient's well-being,' Brown answered. 'We were peaceful here before you came, Christy. You've been a disruptive influence in an old man's life. Don't you think things are best left as they are?'

'You mean go on letting Gramp think I'm married?'

'Well, it's true, isn't it? Oh, my dear, I'm sorry I was so foolish before dinner. I should have known that you wouldn't comply with your grandfather's wishes, because you couldn't. Well, the secret's out, though it was a pity you had to hurl it at him with quite such brutal suddenness.'

Christy sat staring at her and saying nothing.

'You don't like me, Brown, do you? You've never liked me,' she said at last in tones of such naïve surprise that the nurse nearly laughed. She came to sit on the side of the bed. Her eyes were secretive, but her smile was reassuring and professional.

'What nonsense!' she replied briskly. 'Of course I like you, but naturally my patient's well-being comes first.'

'Naturally,' Christy said. 'I don't think I've ever known you, Brown.'

'Have you ever tried to know me?' Brown countered lightly. 'No, why should you? I'm just the nurse, an employee of your grandfather's. Now go to sleep. It's better if you don't try to see him before you go in the morning.'

'You've got me out of the way very neatly, haven't you?' said Christy slowly. 'Are you really after my grandfather and his money? I thought he was just boasting.'

The nurse's lashes were lowered, but her eyebrows lifted a fraction.

'You're tired, or you would never make such an extravagant suggestion,' she said. 'Forget about all this and get back to that nice young man in Cornwall. I'll do my best to smooth things over for you once you've gone.'

'Will you, Brown? I rather think you'll go on fanning the

25

flames.'

'What nonsense! Sir Harry is naturally upset now, but he'll come round, and one day you must bring your husband down here and put everything right.'

'I might at that,' said Christy deliberately, and surprised a fleeting quiver of the older woman's lashes.

'That,' said Rose Brown, getting up and smoothing the creases in her dress, 'would be the most sensible thing to do. Good night.'

CHAPTER TWO

ALL this she was remembering as she sat outside the inn, sipping her shandy, and staring moodily at the fishing smacks with the coloured sails which she so much liked to paint.

Back in the little village of St. Bede it had been easy to forget the whole thing. Brown had assured her before she left that her grandfather's heart attack was not serious, and although the nurse had rather regretfully confirmed the fact that the old man had no wish to see his granddaughter, she in her turn had no wish to see him. Stubborn, high-handed old reprobate, thinking he could buy anyone and anything, she told herself angrily as she started on the long run from Sussex to Cornwall. But soon the sheer pleasure of driving through the early morning in an open car sent most of the unpleasantness from her mind; only that unexpected facet of the nurse's character remained to niggle at her gently. Brown was up to something, and if it was really true that she had a notion of becoming Lady Tavener, she was very neatly disposing of an unwanted heiress by professing to believe that absurd fabrication. Rose Brown? What nonsense! It was only natural that she should resent the intrusion of an unacknowledged granddaughter into their hitherto placid lives, but that was no reason to endow her with mischievous schemes.

It had not been the end of the matter, however. A letter had come from Christy's grandfather, further stressing his displeasure, but desiring to inspect the young man of her choice, to which she paid no attention, for what was there to reply? This was followed up by a telegram which stated simply: *Return at once and bring your man with you.* The message, she knew, must have occasioned a certain amount

27

of comment, via the village post office, but when a second telegram arrived, intimating that if she persisted in ignoring his demands he would make the journey himself, she was thrown into a state of indecision, bordering upon panic. She could recant, of course, but that might place her very firmly in his power, and a brief note from Rose Brown, implying neglect and reproach, made it very clear that whatever the nurse privately believed, she had made no effort to disabuse her patient.

What to do? she thought distractedly, having her first view of the complexities that could arise from unguarded speech and a too lively imagination. She wandered into the inn to replenish her glass. The usual crowd of fishermen and tourists were propping up the bar and they made way for her absently. But today there was a stranger among them, a dark, silent man in shabby fisherman's garb and several days' growth of stubble on his lean, hard-bitten face. He was, she supposed, one of the crew of the smart little cabin cruiser which had put into the harbour the day before, and was aware that he watched her with idle curiosity as she waited for her glass to be filled.

'Who's the blonde?' she heard him ask as she went back to her seat on the terrace, and flushed slightly as she caught the landlord's reply: 'Just one of they mazed artist foreigners—rents Jim Trevone's place along the hard. More money than sense, I'd say, but she'm a decent enough little maid for all her paint and fancy pants.'

The stranger came out on to the terrace a few minutes later, carrying his tankard of ale.

'Are you too decent to pass the time of day with another foreigner?' he asked, propping himself against the low balustrade which surmounted the seawall.

She looked at him coolly, raising polite eyebrows.

'You heard what he said, didn't you?' he observed conversationally, and she did not altogether care for the hint of mockery in his cool, rather sleepy eyes.

'I heard you ask who the blonde was, too,' she retorted. 'Perhaps you had mistaken this pub for one of those low waterfront dives.'

The mockery deepened to amusement in his eyes.

'What would a girl like you know about low waterfront dives?' he asked. 'This isn't a pick-up, you know. Perhaps you would prefer to come inside again and get the landlord to introduce us.'

She was aware that he was laughing at her, and aware, too, that he was distracting her from the problem on hand.

'Not at all,' she replied. 'One can pass the time of day with anyone in a pub.'

'Too true. Would you have a cigarette handy?'

She tossed him the open packet lying beside her glass and watched his hands as he selected one: well-shaped hands, but calloused and stained with oil and dirt.

'Not in my party dress, am I?' he said, observing her regard, while he cupped the flame from a lighted match to his cigarette. The flame highlighted the hollows under his cheekbones for a moment, revealing unkindly the speckle of grey in the dark stubble on his chin.

'Are you from the cabin cruiser down there?' she asked curiously, and he nodded.

'Neat little job, isn't she—or wouldn't you know?'

'Oh, I know a bit about boats. Who's the owner?'

His eyebrows lifted a fraction. They were odd eyebrows, thick and untidy and unsymmetrical. When he raised them, one shot up higher than the other.

'You wouldn't know him,' he replied. 'Anyway it doesn't matter; she was only chartered, and the cruise is over.'

'Oh.' She saw the patches on his rather threadbare trousers and the frayed toes of the dirty sneakers which he wore on his bare feet. 'Are you out of a job, then?'

'Out of a job?' For a moment he sounded surprised, then he suddenly grinned and the whole expression on his face altered. 'Yes, I suppose you might call it that. You, on the

29

other hand, are self-supporting, I understand. Does art pay?'

'Art?'

'These pictures you paint, or whatever it is. Our landlord seemed to think you are a young woman of substance.'

'Do you want to make a touch?' she inquired with quite devastating frankness, and his eyes narrowed, weighing her up.

'Why? Would you be willing to be a sucker?'

'No.'

'What a very curious young woman you are.' There was a faint suggestion of an accent in his speech at times; it could have been American. 'Are strange men in the habit of trying to touch you?'

'Only very rarely. I can usually size them up.'

'Can you really?' He swallowed the rest of his drink at a gulp and set the empty mug down beside her half-finished shandy.

'Sorry I can't offer to treat you,' he said, and turned the empty pockets of his disreputable trousers inside out.

'Would you like me to treat *you*?' she asked, grateful to be diverted for the moment from her unquiet thoughts.

'Not today, thank you.' He disengaged his hard, lean body from the wall and stood looking down at her, his hands thrust into his jacket pockets.

'You are a very imprudent and rather high-handed young lady, Miss——?' he said, and paused suggestively.

'Tavener,' she said, out of sheer surprise.

'How very curious,' he replied unexpectedly, and lounged back into the bar.

The next time she saw him he had shaved and had a haircut, which made him look younger, but he was wearing the same stained trousers and shabby jersey, and the cabin cruiser was at her same berth, so she concluded he still had employment.

'Hullo!' she greeted him with her wide smile. She had

forgotten that he had made her feel uncomfortable, or perhaps his freshly shaven face had given him an air of reassurance.

'Good morning, Miss Tavener,' he replied formally, and paused to look over her shoulder. 'Good God! What's that supposed to be?'

She had set up her easel in the lee of some rocks on the shore and was trying to capture on canvas a small ketch anchored across a path of sunlight on the water, nets spread across the deck to dry. The colours were so clear in her mind's eye that she thought she had reproduced them.

'It's not much good, is it?' she said disconsolately. 'It's so *frustrating* not to get things right when it looks so easy.'

'Well——' he began doubtfully, pulling at his lower lip. 'Do you hope to make a living by this?'

'Of course not—I only dabble. I know I'm no good, but I like to *do* something.'

'I should have thought there were many other ways for an intelligent young woman to earn a living.'

'But I don't need to earn a living. I just like to be doing something,' she repeated seriously, slightly hurt by the remembered glint of mockery in his eyes.

'Of course, I was forgetting—you're the poor little rich girl,' he said, and she frowned.

'I don't give myself airs on that score,' she snapped. 'Anyway, how did you know?'

'Presumably the whole village knows,' he replied with a shrug. 'You're probably one of St. Bede's minor showpieces—the young heiress who chooses to rent a fisherman's cottage and lives the simple life alone.'

'I'm hardly an heiress,' she protested uncomfortably. 'At least not in the sense you mean.'

'In what sense, then?'

Fairmile, Gramp, the muddle that was building up from her lies began to crowd in on her again.

'Oh, you wouldn't understand,' she told him crossly, and

31

he lifted an eyebrow.

'Are you in some kind of a jam?' he inquired conversationally.

'No, not exactly—well, yes, in a way.'

'Well, make your mind up. Some strange remarks are circulating in the village.'

'You've been making inquiries about me, haven't you?' she asked him accusingly, but he only laughed and began scuffing in the soft sand with a toe which now protruded through the canvas of his shoe.

'No need to inquire, what with all these telegrams and things. Here's one now,' he said, and tossed a crumpled official envelope into her lap.

'How did you come to have it?' she asked suspiciously, snatching it.

'Understandable error on the part of the postmistress, I imagine. Same name,' he said.

She was hardly listening as she read the telegram. It was from Brown and said: *Advise you do not delay. Possibility of change of heart re Fairmile should your choice be approved.*

'Oh hell, oh hell! Oh buckets of blood!' she exclaimed distractedly. 'What were you saying about names?'

'I said the name was the same, which explained why the postmistress gave the thing to me,' he repeated patiently.

She continued to stare at him, her thoughts confused. He had read the telegram, of course, not that it could have made much sense to him. The ribbon had slipped off her pony-tail, and the breeze blew the pale cloud of hair across her face.

'Much better,' he said, approvingly. 'You've got pretty hair—fine and light like candy-floss.'

She did not think it odd, then, that he should have become personal. The eyes regarding her appeared wholly disinterested.

'What *is* your name?' she asked, forgetting that this was

32

only the second time she had met him.

'Tavener,' he replied with a grin, and walked away.

She stared after him with her mouth wide open. He was making it up, of course, as an excuse for having opened her telegram. He was, she judged, the sort of man who would enjoy making sudden and probably untrue statements for the sake of discomfiture. Savagely she slashed a brush across the canvas, making havoc of the morning's work, and began packing up her gear.

Brown's telegram burnt a hole in her pocket. She had invented this ridiculous situation on the spur of the moment, never doubting that she could retreat gracefully when the time came. But was the future of Fairmile, after all, going to depend on the successful structure of a lie?

She dumped her gear in the cottage, noting at the same time that it looked due for a thorough clean-up; then, finding she was out of cigarettes, went along to the inn to get some more. She felt lonely and disenchanted. The cottage had been fun to begin with and the self-imposed chores a novelty, but now with the summer ending and the empty months stretching ahead, life did not appear so carefree and exciting.

As she passed the little general shop on the hard, the postmistress hailed her, proffering yet another telegram.

'Seems someone's anxious about you, m'dear, or maybe it's you who should be worrying,' she remarked a trifle sourly, and Christy read the latest message with a sinking heart.

This time it was from her grandfather, intimating at extravagant length that owing to his doctor's most recent pronouncement it would be suicidal for him to make the journey into Cornwall. All might be forgiven if she and that scoundrel would return for his blessing. He was an old man and time was short. He and she must sink their pride.

'Oh dear, oh lord!' Christy exclaimed, defeated, stuffing

33

the telegram into the pocket of her jeans. Gramp, she suspected, would try any gambit to get what he wanted, but it was just possible that the reference to his health might be true. Had not Brown warned her that his heart was none too strong?

The little bar was empty when she went in to ask for her cigarettes, and the landlord greeted her with his usual friendly incuriousness.

'What'll it be, miss? Have one on the house,' he said, glad to see a familiar face, for trade was falling off now the tourist season had nearly ended.

She did not want a drink, but did not like to refuse, so settled for a tomato juice.

'You'll be packing up soon, I reckon, miss,' he observed, helping himself to a pint of mild. 'Wanted at home, I understand.'

'Yes,' she said, not troubling to deny that she had a home to go to. Her affairs were obviously becoming public property as far as St. Bede was concerned.

'Not bad news, I hope—this last telegram?' he offered tentatively, and she gave him her sudden wide smile.

'You probably know just as well as I do what was in the telegram, Joe,' she retorted. 'Tell me—that man who's been in here, off the cabin cruiser in the harbour—is his name really the same as mine?'

'So I believe. Coincidence, bain't it? Asked quite a bit about you, too. Would 'e be a long-lost relative, should you reckon?'

'Very unlikely,' she replied a little shortly, and flushed as the object of their speculations pushed open the swing door from the street.

He took no notice of her, but ordered himself a beer which he carried to the further end of the bar counter, where he propped himself and gazed absently at the smoke-discoloured ceiling while he drank.

Christy was relieved when two or three of the 'regulars'

joined them and conversation became general, but she continued to perch on the stool in her corner, not wishing to go back to the solitude of the cottage and her own uneasy thoughts.

Presently she became aware that the dark stranger was standing at her elbow and had pushed his empty tankard suggestively across the counter.

'Would you care to repeat your offer of yesterday and treat me, Miss Tavener?' he inquired lazily.

She ordered a drink for him, but looked at him coldly, hoping to prick the assurance with which he so blatantly advertised his penuriousness, but he only grinned and lifted his foaming mug in salute.

'*Slainte*,' he said. 'I'll return the compliment one of these days.'

'*Slainte?*' she repeated, creasing her smooth forehead. The salutation was new to her, used as she was to the idiom of more cosmopolitan countries.'

'An Irish form of greeting,' he replied, and she said, remembering the faint intonation in his speech which had puzzled her:

'Oh, is that your nationality?'

'Only very remotely. There's a lot of mixed blood in Canada—mostly French—Scots, too—so you can take your pick of my mongrel ancestry.'

'So you're from Canada? Have you worked a passage over, or something?'

He saw her glancing at his calloused hands and laughed.

'Well, not in a small cabin cruiser,' he retorted mildly, and she gave a little wriggle of discomfiture. For a young man with no apparent substance he had a disconcerting knack of disturbing one's composure.

'I think I will have a proper drink, after all,' she said, pushing aside the tomato juice and ordering a gin and tonic.

The stranger did not offer to pay and she pushed some coins across the counter, feeling irrationally annoyed.

'You know,' he remarked conversationally, 'you would seem to me to be rather an intolerant young person. You jump to an awful lot of conclusions, don't you?'

'Do I?' she replied uncertainly. Then a beautiful idea popped straight into her head, and before she could give herself time to think she was rushing into speech.

'Would you be interested in a business proposition, Mr. —Mr. Tavener?' she asked, and his eyebrows rose.

'Well, now, that's rather a curious question for a young lady to put to a perfect stranger in a public house, isn't it?' he said, a slight drawl betraying more definitely his Canadian origin.

'I said business—*strictly* business,' she replied with a certain tartness, and he smiled faintly and said nothing.

'You're in need of a job. I'm in need of a husband,' she said, and his eyes suddenly lost their laziness.

'I *beg* your pardon?'

'Oh, only temporarily,' she continued hastily. 'You see, as you guessed this morning, I'm in a jam. I can pay—I can pay well. Five hundred, would you say, for two or three weeks? That should tide you over for a bit, shouldn't it? Having the same name does seem to be a kind of omen, I mean, and solves a lot of difficulties—like signing cheques and things. I do hope it's all quite clear.'

'Not very,' he replied somewhat dryly. 'But perhaps this is hardly the place for such startling revelations.'

'Will you come back to the cottage with me?' she asked impulsively. 'I can knock up an omelette or something for lunch. Then I can explain everything.'

'I fancy you'll have to do quite a bit of explaining, young lady,' he said, and she did not altogether care for the new inflection in his voice.

'Well, are you interested?' she snapped impatiently, anxious to acquire the upper hand once more.

'One should always be interested in a good business proposition,' he retorted, the drawl reappearing. 'Five hundred pounds, did you say? I should naturally require to know exactly what I was letting myself in for.'

'Naturally,' she replied coldly. 'The arrangement would be purely impersonal and I—I should require a written undertaking from you to that effect.'

The muscles tightened perceptibly about his rather hard mouth, and for a moment she thought he looked as though he would like to slap her.

'You have,' he said with deceptive mildness, 'the most unmitigated gall of anyone I've yet met. Let's go.'

Back in the cottage she set about making preparations for a meal, doing her best to ignore him, but uncomfortably aware of his lazy regard as she moved backwards and forwards beween the kitchen and the tiny living-room. He did not offer to help her, neither did he make any effort to bridge the uneasy silence which had fallen between them. When she went to the kitchen to make the omelette he followed and watched while she broke eggs angrily into a basin to beat.

'You've forgotten the tablespoonful of cold water,' he observed, prodding the toast which was starting to burn.

'I don't make them that way,' she replied shortly, rescuing the toast too late.

'You should. It makes all the difference. The pan isn't hot enough yet. The fat should smoke.'

'Will you please move out of the way so that I can get at the stove?'

She poured the egg mixture into the pan, but it broke and stuck and came away in blackened pieces instead of a smooth golden-brown envelope.

'See what I mean? No water,' he said with irritating complacency.

'Perhaps you could make one better yourself,' she snapped, carrying the plates into the living-room and banging them on the table.

'Oh, I could undoubtedly,' he replied, 'but I was forgetting I'm your guest. Would you like me to mix the salad?'

'If you like. I don't bother with a dressing myself.'

'A crude taste. You might as well be a rabbit.'

He mixed the salad with a practised hand, piled some on to both their plates and sat down opposite her.

'May we begin?' he asked politely. 'Omelettes go leathery so quickly.'

She looked across at him, aware suddenly that her hair was disordered and her face unbecomingly flushed from the heat of the stove and her own ruffled feelings, and catching the unexpected twinkle in his eyes, smiled reluctantly.

'That's better,' he said in the same tone of approval he had used on the shore when the ribbon had freed her hair in the wind. 'You take yourself very seriously, don't you?'

'Not really, but you're—you're something a little new in my experience, I suppose.'

'Well, you're certainly something new in mine! I can't say I've ever been propositioned before!'

'I didn't mean it as a joke or—or a disreputable proposal,' she said stiffly, and he sent her a swift, speculative glance.

'Strictly business, of course. Doesn't anyone ever pull your leg?' he retorted mildly and, unexpectedly, she felt at ease with him. He might be a rolling stone and out of a job, but she was beginning to suspect that he was not entirely the tough opportunist he had allowed her to think him.

'I don't know many people—intimately, that is. Perhaps that's why——' she began, sounding suddenly shy, and he gave her another quick glance.

'How old are you?' he asked abruptly.

'Twenty.'

'That probably accounts for it.'

'Accounts for what?'

'That shattering assumption that money gives you the right to crack the whip. You're a bit young to be gallivanting about alone, advertising your wealth to all and sundry.'

'Do I do that?' She sounded humble and he regarded her thoughtfully.

'Perhaps it's unconscious, or you're rather new to it, or perhaps you haven't as much wealth as you like to pretend,' he replied a little dryly. Her resentment returned.

'I'm rich enough to pay you five hundred pounds for services rendered,' she retorted, trying to sound grown up. 'Or isn't it enough?'

'That I can't tell you until I've gone into the matter,' he said. 'But now, I beg of you. We shall have indigestion if we discuss business while we eat. If you have any more eggs I'll go and make us a proper omelette. I'm still hungry.'

She had to admit that his omelette was vastly superior to hers, as also was his technique with the washing up once the meal was over.

'You seem to be quite domesticated,' she told him when the last piece of crockery had been put away and the tea-cloths hung out to dry in the sun.

'Oh, we learn to be handy in the backwoods,' he said, and she wondered if he was one of those shiftless hobos one read about, washing dishes in rough eating-houses for the price of a meal. She had only a very hazy idea as to how one would set about earning a living in the backwoods of Canada.

'Now,' he said, 'you can spill the beans, and after that I'll tell you if I'm prepared to take you up on your offer.'

It had never occurred to her that he might refuse. Five hundred pounds was, after all, a lot of money to be paid for simply spending a week or so in comfort.

'I don't know where to begin,' she said a little helplessly, aware, now, that it might not be easy to convince this stranger who seemed to have such contempt for wealth that the whole situation between herself and her grandfather was anything but a fanciful absurdity.

'Begin at the beginning,' he said encouragingly. 'What's

your name for a start?'

'Christy—Christobel, really—only I've always thought that sounded prim and old-fashioned.'

'I think it's rather charming, but if you fancy it I shall address you as Christobel when you annoy me. Proceed, please.'

Suddenly it was quite easy to talk to him. The story came tumbling out in anything but chronological order, but he was a good listener and seldom interrupted, and at the end he sat observing her in silence for a while.

'Well now,' he said. 'Let me get it straight. Your grandfather is the old-fashioned villain of the piece who, cheated of sons and heirs, wants to marry you off to some man of his choice.'

'He's not,' she interrupted, screwing her slim body into a still smaller space as her arms tightened about her knees; 'not the villain of the piece, I mean. He just has a thing about the Taveners and the fact that the name may die out. He's rather a poppet, really, but stubborn—stubborn as hell!'

'A poppet with a strange turn of humour, in this day and age. However, let's return to our muttons. He didn't see fit to acknowledge you until you returned to England and looked him up; but now that he's old and crippled, he starts making demands.'

'It isn't quite like that, either. I—I must have given you a wrong impression of Gramp. He—he's a quite friendly sort of tyrant who's always had his own way, but I can be pigheaded, too.'

'I can well believe it,' he retorted dryly. 'Well, then, you're fond of the old boy, but you're not prepared to give in to his whims, even for the sake of this doubtful inheritance. I've got that right, have I?'

'Yes, only—well, the whole thing's so absurd, really. I used to think it was a kind of joke—advertising for possible relatives, I mean, and then picking one out of the blue and dangling him in front of my nose in exchange for Fairmile. I don't want his money, but Fairmile is my right. I'm the only one left,' she said, and he regarded her thoughtfully, aware that for the moment she was herself, an honest, rather bewildered child, passionately in love with an ideal.

'This place, Fairmile—why is it so important to you?' he asked gently.

'I don't quite know. I was born there, and though I was only six when we left, I never forgot it. In all our years abroad, after my mother had married again, she used to talk of it constantly. She pined a little, I think, even though she was happy with my stepfather. I suppose she brought me up to believe that Fairmile would one day be mine because I was the last of the line.'

'Yes, well, that all sounds very nice, if slightly archaic, but what possessed you to suddenly invent a mythical husband? You must have known that would ditch the inheritance.'

'I didn't think. I didn't care—I just said the first thing that came into my head to—to shut him up. Actually, I suppose Brown had already sown the seeds, without knowing it.'

'Ah yes, the nurse,' he murmured, and his eyes were lazy again. 'Were you suggesting earlier that this Brown female had an interest in cutting you out, according to the best traditions of fiction?'

'You think I'm making it all up, don't you?' she said a little angrily.

'Not at all—that is, only with reservations,' he countered smoothly. 'But you did imply, I thought, that the nurse might have ideas of her own regarding your grandfather.'

'Grump boasted that Brown had a mind to marry him, but that was only to goad me, I think.'

'Then what made you change your opinion?'

'I don't know. The way she behaved that last evening, I suppose. I thought she was trying to get me out of the way,

41

but perhaps it was all nonsense. Don't think, Mr. Tavener, that I blame her if she's after Gramp and his money. She's a good nurse and would probably make him a good wife, but Fairmile——'

'So we come back to Fairmile,' he said softly. 'And because you've got yourself tangled in the results of a foolish lie, you want someone to help you to play the farce out. Really, Miss Christobel Tavener, I don't know whether to take you on trust or make a rude comment on the whole ridiculous business.'

'I'm afraid you'll have to take me on trust,' she replied quite meekly. 'The only lie I've told was that silly one to Gramp, and that was only one of those fantastic statements one flings out in a rage. I never thought he'd believe me.'

'Then why couldn't you have come clean and said so?'

'I don't know. I thought, I suppose, that Brown was going to smooth the way after I'd gone, for I didn't imagine *she* believed me, but—well, I've shown you the letters and telegrams, and I can't be sure—I can't be *sure*, you see, whether Gramp is just shooting a line or—or whether his health really *is* cracking up.'

'I see. You're genuinely fond of him, aren't you?'

'Yes—yes, I am. His autocratic notions infuriate me, he's rude and selfish and a bully, and has never done anything for any of us, but—well, he's the only one I've got, now.'

'Just a poor little rich girl, after all,' he mocked, and she felt he had suddenly withdrawn the sympathy which, perhaps, she had only imagined.

'I'm not so rich as all that—just comfortable,' she retorted. 'Well, are you going to help me, Mr. Tavener? Five hundred pounds is quite a lot of money and, if you don't mind my saying so, you look as if you could use it.'

He crossed one shabbily clad leg over the other deliberately.

'You should never assume things about strangers, Christobel,' he observed with a return of the drawl. 'Neither should you judge them by their attire. Besides, it's not very polite to draw attention to someone's obvious lack of means, is it?'

'I'm sorry,' she said, looking away. 'I didn't mean to be rude. I just thought——'

'You just thought that money could buy most things. You must be a chip off the old block from all accounts.'

She felt her colour rising and reached hastily for a cigarette.

'If you don't want to earn a bit of easy money then we'd better forget about it,' she said stiffly, and his eyebrows rose, one, as always, lifted higher than the other.

'I didn't say that,' he countered calmly. 'When did you propose paying over this money, might I ask?'

She smoked furiously, avoiding his eyes.

'Two hundred and fifty down and the other half at the end of the contract,' she said promptly. 'I'll write you a cheque now, if you like.'

'Well, now, you do just that. If this once bounces, I imagine I can always come down on your granddad,' he said.

She did not trust herself to reply but jumped up to rummage for her cheque book and a pen.

'What initials?' she snapped.

'J.R.,' he replied imperturbably. 'My first name's Josiah. It's just as well to be familiar with your husband's Christian name.'

'*Josiah!* Oh, no, it *can't* be!' She barely repressed an undignified giggle and he gave her a glance of reproof.

'What's wrong with it? It's a perfectly good Biblical name. Anyway, I'm generally known as Joss. Get on with filling in that cheque before I change my mind.'

She frowned as she wrote her own familiar surname on the cheque and suddenly looked up at him with widening eyes.

'You don't—it couldn't be that you are one of our vague

relatives, after all?' she said on a faint note of horror. He grinned unkindly.

'Not a chance,' he replied. 'Tavener isn't even my real name, so I believe. I came out of an orphanage near a dead-and-alive little place called Tavener's Creek and they named me after that.'

For a moment she suspected him of pulling her leg again, but his eyes were quite serious and he took the cheque from her with a sardonic little smile, scrutinized it, folded it carefully and thrust it into a trouser pocket.

'Well, you're the boss,' he said. 'Where do we go from here?'

CHAPTER THREE

It was decided that they should travel to Sussex the following week and Christy sent a telegram to that effect to her grandfather. Joss said he had one or two matters to attend to first in London and would, therefore, leave the next day, but when Christy suggested they should drive up together to save him the railway fare, he replied:

'I think not. We will arrange a rendezvous in town, when the time comes. Don't look so suspicious, my dear, I shan't run away. Besides, you can always stop that cheque.'

'Yes, I suppose I can,' she said doubtfully. 'It isn't exactly that I don't trust you, Mr. Tavener, but we are complete strangers.'

'Why should you trust me?' he retorted. 'And hadn't you better get used to calling me Joss—or Josiah, if you prefer it?'

He could, without the slightest justification, make her feel very uncomfortable, she thought.

'Have you somewhere to go to in London?' she asked, striving after politeness.

'Oh yes. Besides, you know, there are always the doss-houses—or even the Embankment at a pinch.'

She smiled uncertainly.

'Now you're laughing at me.'

'Possibly people haven't laughed at you enough. You're rather absurd, you know.'

'Am I?' she said a little wistfully. 'I wasn't trying to be nosey. I was—I was only concerned that you should have somewhere comfortable to stay.'

'Thank you,' he replied gravely. 'I can see that we shall both have to learn a little tolerance of each other's random remarks. Will you be going to London, too?'

'Yes. I must collect some clothes. I've nothing much down here,' she said, and blushed as she realized he might be wondering how to deal with the matter of his own wardrobe.

He grinned at her unkindly.

'Don't worry, I'll get my decent suit out of hock,' he told her and, from feeling sorry for him, she immediately wanted to hit him.

Before he left they exchanged addresses where they might get in touch; his, she saw, was care of a firm of solicitors in the City. When he had gone and she began packing up to leave the cottage, it almost seemed as if the whole crazy scheme might have been a dream, but, oddly enough, she missed him in the little inn of an evening and remembered that, after all, he had never bought her a drink.

'Joe——' she said to the landlord on her last evening, 'would you say I was gullible?'

He frowned, wiping his glasses with methodical care.

'Taken in, would you be meaning?' he asked.

'Yes, I suppose so. Only——'

'Only you thought you was the one with all the tricks, eh, miss?'

'Yes—and that's true, too. But not tricks *as* tricks, Joe. Legitimate business.'

The landlord's cheeks creased in fat folds as he smiled at her with sly indulgence.

'Don't try tricks with the likes of 'e, m'dear,' he said with a chuckle. 'Up to anyone's games, Mr. Tavener be, I shouldn't wonder. Any relation of yours, miss?'

'Well, he says not.'

'Then 'e b'ain't. Leave 'e be, miss. 'E's gone to Lunnon, anyways, and you'm leaving tomorrow, so I understand.'

'Yes. I'll miss St. Bede and the pub and you, Joe.'

'Find a good man, m'dear. T'isn't right or natural for a little maid like you to be trapesing round the country alone. Tourists, yes—but you'm better than they, I should hope.'

46

Christy gazed into her empty glass, feeling small and chidden. She liked Joe and wanted his approval. She had not felt herself to be a tourist, established for the summer in Jim Trevone's cottage, but she realized now, that once she was gone, although the villagers might think of her kindly, they would scarcely miss her, for she had never been part of their lives.

'Good-bye, Joe,' she said, and got up abruptly to go.

'Good-bye, m'dear,' he replied with comfortable indifference. 'We'll see you next summer, maybe.'

She walked back along the waterfront, out of humour with her summer's freedom, and knew a nostalgia for Fairmile, her rightful anchorage, and even for the doubtful support of the stranger who might, by virtue of his name and supposed standing, help to set a final seal on her inheritance. Only then did it seriously occur to her that she had probably said good-bye to two hundred and fifty pounds and would be left to explain the tangle to her grandfather as best she could.

She drove to London the next day, wryly convinced that she was unlikely to hear from Mr. Josiah Tavener again. It was too late to stop the cheque and, although he had himself proffered the suggestion, that had only been his cleverness. He had, no doubt, no more believed her story than he had expected her to believe his. Even his name, which he had admitted was not really his own, must have been thought of on the spur of the moment to soften her up in case a hard luck tale should be needed.

'One born every minute!' she told herself derisively, just as he, no doubt, had said, and was astonished and suddenly absurdly excited to find a letter from him waiting for her at the flat. He would meet her, he said, by the Achilles Statue in Hyde Park in three days' time at two-thirty precisely. Should she have changed her mind in the meantime, she was to notify the above firm of solicitors immediately, although, since this would amount to breach of contract, she

47

could scarcely expect the return of her initial payment.

The intervening days passed in a whirl of appointments with hairdressers and shops and entertaining the two friends who shared the flat. For Christy the excitement mounted; she was embarked on adventure and, if her grandfather was to be deceived in the process, it was his own fault for being so importunate in the matter of her marriage.

On the appointed day she drove to Hyde Park, half expecting that Joss would not turn up at all. She parked the car neatly and sat for a moment, enjoying the sunshine and the busy noise of traffic in Park Lane, then got out and walked leisurely towards the Achilles Statue.

At first she did not see him, for she had been looking subconsciously for a shabbily dressed figure, and she jumped when, her attention distracted by two well-worn and much labelled suitcases placed tidily by a park bench, his voice observed with its familiar tinge of mockery:

'Did you think I'd ratted on you?'

She looked up at him and her eyes widened in naïve surprise which she made no effort to conceal. He looked, she thought, like any other prosperous young businessman taking time off from his affairs in the sunshine. His clothes were good, his well-polished shoes obviously hand-made and, despite the conventional excellence of his attire, he looked somehow more formidable that he had when clad in the rough fisherman's garb she remembered.

'Oh!' she said, eyeing him with evident surprise, and he grinned unkindly.

'My sartorial elegance has shaken you, I can see,' he said. 'I told you I'd get my best suit out of hock. Your own transformation is encouraging too, let me add.'

He had, of course, only seen her in jeans. The simple but expensive little dress, with its equally expensive accessories, the smart shoes and freshly styled hair had given her a feeling of superiority when she set out, but, under his cool stare, she experienced a slight ripple of discomfort, despite the implied compliment.

'Shall we go?' she said, trying to sound dignified, but he pulled her unceremoniously on to the bench beside his suit-cases and sat down himself.

'Hadn't you better brief me first?' he asked.

'Brief you?'

'Well, this inheritance you're hoping for and my—er—grandparent by marriage are only very hazy sketches in my mind's eye. It would be a pity if I put both feet in for want of a little information, wouldn't it?'

'Yes—yes, of course,' she said, and, because it was suddenly pleasant sitting on a park bench with him in the sunlight, the story of her affection for Fairmile, for her grandfather, came tumbling out and, as she talked, her sense of authority returned, so that she could warn him quite calmly of possible pitfalls and reassure him on matters which could be taken for granted.

'For,' she said, 'Gramp knows very little about me, really, so you can hardly be tripped up on that score, and you can find your own answers to any questions about yourself—only don't forget to tell me what line you're adopting in case I invent one of my own.'

'You're pretty good, I imagine, at inventing lines,' he observed politely, and the trace of that Canadian drawl was back in his voice.

'Well, I've landed myself in a situation, I've got to give colour to it, haven't I?' she retorted, and he smiled.

'Very true. Lies are bedfellows, you know, Christobel.'

'It wasn't a lie in that sense—not deliberate, I mean. It was a sort of nonsense I got myself mixed up in.'

'You could have explained.'

'I told you, Brown wouldn't let me see him. Also—well, I may have been wrong about Brown.'

'The scheming little nurse, wanting you out of the way?'

'Of course she isn't. It's just——'

'It's just that she didn't react as you expected and get you out of the mess.'

'No, she didn't.'

'Well,' said Joss reasonably, 'why should she? If you hadn't managed to convince her of the truth, she was scarcely likely to interfere, in her position, was she?'

'No, I suppose not, only——'

'Only what?'

'Oh, nothing. I'd got her wrong, I expect. You see, Mr. Tavener'—Christy's eyes widened in naïve discovery—'I've always taken Brown for granted. I—I didn't expect her to have opinions of her own.'

'Very short-sighted of you,' he replied dryly. 'And you really must stop addressing me as Mr. Tavener. I thought Christian names came easily to your generation.'

'What do you mean—*my* generation?' she asked suspiciously. 'How old are *you*, anyway?'

'Thirty-five, and definitely a square, I imagine you would say.'

'I'm no cool cat, myself. Wouldn't you—mightn't you have a wife by now?'

'I might, but I haven't. Not that a little detail like that would worry you for present purposes, I imagine.'

'I've only just thought of it,' she said with frank surprise. 'You must have rather a low opinion of me, Mr.—I mean, Joss.'

'I hardly know you well enough to form an opinion,' he replied coolly. 'Any more I should know? Well, then, perhaps we might be going. Oh, and incidentally, you'd better put this on.' He dived into his breast pocket and produced a wedding ring.

'Oh, I quite forgot,' she exclaimed, and slipped the ring on to her finger with an uneasy sense of superstition.

'Does it fit? I had to make a guess.'

'Near enough—but it's the genuine thing, isn't it? You

could have got one at Woolworths.'

'Oh no,' he said with a grin. 'From all you've told me, your revered grandpa would be the first to recognize dross from gold.'

'Then you must let me pay,' she said, her nose in the air. 'I don't want you to incur any expense on my account.'

'I think not,' he replied with a faint twinkle. 'I prefer to make that small gesture myself, and I can just afford it. Shall we go?'

As they drove down to Sussex, Christy, for the first time, felt herself committed to an act of rashness from which there was now no drawing back. What did she know of this stranger beside her, and could she successfully carry off this masquerade under the disapproving eye of her grandfather and the more subtle speculations of Rose Brown? Joss himself, she began to suspect, was not going to prove a mere cipher in the arrangement.

Several times she glanced from his dark profile to his steady, experienced hands on the wheel. He drove fast and expertly, and she wondered again about his private life, what he had done for a living before coming to England, whether that well-tailored suit had been bought with part of her two hundred and fifty pounds, and what he had done with the rest of it.

But soon she had reverted again to Fairmile; the chestnut avenue, the maze where, as a child, she had once got lost, the old drag which nearly a century ago had carried Taveners to church on Sundays and still stood in the coach-house, the two white peacocks which had once strutted on the terrace and now stood stuffed and incongruous on either side of the marble staircase.

'You've made a kind of fairy tale for yourself, haven't you?' he said, and she frowned.

'I don't think so. Fairmile's real. Perhaps when you travel about a lot from place to place you hang on to the idea of something permanent.'

'Perhaps. How did you get your schooling if you were always moving around?'

'Oh, they sent me home to England for that. My step-father was half Italian, but he had very rigid notions about English education. As a matter of fact I think I was rather in the way. They were very happy, you see.'

'Did you spend any of your holidays with your grandfather?' he asked, probing more gently, for he thought she might not have been wanted.

'No,' she replied, and added without rancour: 'Gramp couldn't forgive me for not being a boy, neither could he forgive my mother for marrying what he chose to call a damn dago. He must have been a mean old cuss till sickness mellowed him.'

'In my experience, sickness seldom mellows people!' he returned with his usual dryness. 'I suspect that that rather high-handed quality you seem to possess took him by surprise—or perhaps it was a compliment to himself.'

She lifted a little uneasily in her seat, and the wind blew a long strand of hair across her eyes, making her blink.

'Would you call me high-handed?' she asked with sudden meekness, and saw him smile.

'Well, shall we say that wealth and sudden independence has gone a little to your head,' he replied, swerving to avoid a cyclist so that she was momentarily thrown against his shoulder.

'Don't you think you take rather a lot upon yourself for an employed person, Josiah?' she countered sharply. This time his smile became a grin.

'Oh, I wouldn't say that,' he replied equably. 'The fact that you're employing me doesn't put a stopper on my opinions. Also, your grandfather will expect a certain amount of divergence in a newly-married couple, I imagine.'

'Joss,' she said, giving him an uncertain glance, 'this is a strictly commercial proposition. No funny business, you understand.'

'Now why should you think there might be funny business?' he inquired mildly. 'Are you so accustomed to assaults being made upon your virtue?'

'Yes, I am,' she retorted defiantly. 'Most men make passes when you're reasonably good-looking, and money always adds to the attraction.'

'A cynic at twenty? Poor Christobel—poor little rich girl,' he said without a hint of sympathy, and she felt unaccustomed tears sting her eyelids.

'You,' she said, 'are an absolute beast, I think!'

'That's better,' he observed approvingly, as he had on two other occasions. 'You sound more as you're meant to be.'

'And what's that?'

'A nice little girl with natural likes and dislikes. How much further?'

'Not far,' she said and, forgetting he was a stranger, eagerly pointed out the familiar places, promising to show him this or that favourite spot, adding as a rather wistful after-thought that perhaps he would not be interested.

'How young are you,' he commented with a brief, impatient sigh. Then he said gently: 'Yes, Christy, I should like to become acquainted with the delights of your childhood—or is it really your mother's childhood?'

'Mostly hers, I suppose, but it's all got muddled up. I was very little when I was here, but I seem to remember so much. Look, here's Fairmile! Isn't the avenue splendid? It's almost a straight mile, you know, and when the chestnuts are in flower people come for miles to look at it.'

'Very impressive,' he remarked as he turned the car in at the lodge gates, but he observed the moss on the drive, the roughly trimmed verges and the gaps in the fencing which separated the parkland. Sir Harry Tavener, for all his reputed wealth, appeared as unable as most people today to preserve his estate as it once had been.

The house, with its tall Tudor chimneys, was not so very big, after all, but it lay long and rosy in the evening light, and its many windows catching the sun gave the lie to first impressions. Fairmile might not be classed as one of the more famous stately homes, but it was too large to accommodate only one old man and his nurse and a visiting granddaughter.

'I see what you mean,' Joss said, drawing up neatly before the open front door.

'You like it?' Christy asked with naïve pleasure. 'You can see it's an inheritance to be proud of—to fight for?'

'One is prepared to fight for precious little that is tangible,' he observed obscurely and with a certain chill, but before she could think of something with which to retaliate, old Tom had hurried out on to the porch, followed by Mrs. Heap, her fat face moist with emotion.

Both exclaimed and fussed and offered congratulations, looking expectantly and curiously at Joss, and Christy heard herself saying for the first time:

'This is my—my husband,' and felt that she blushed at putting the lie at last into words.

She had to admire Joss's cool acceptance of his role, however. There may have been a glint of mockery in his eyes, but his manner was impeccable. He shook hands, made the right rejoinders and even professed himself lucky to have won such a charming bride.

'That's going a bit far!' Christy muttered, kicking him surreptitiously on the shin, but she could see that Mrs. Heap was completely captivated, and her reproachful inquiry as to why they had all been kept in the dark about this surprise marriage clearly required no answer.

'Where's Gramp?' Christy asked, but before she could have a reply, Rose Brown came hurrying down the stairs and across the hall with hands outstretched.

'Christy, my dear, welcome home!' she cried softly, and took the girl in her arms.

Christy could not remember ever having been kissed by the nurse before; indeed, she thought Brown was putting on a very gracious and convincing impersonation of mistress of the house. She returned the kiss more warmly than she felt because she was chiding herself for uncharitable reflections, then turned hastily towards Joss.

'This is Nurse Brown, Joss. I've told you about her,' she said a little brusquely, and saw the flicker of surprise, or was it calculation, come into the nurse's eyes.

'Well,' said Brown, holding out a hand, 'you didn't prepare us for this sort of surprise, Christy! Your grandfather will have to withdraw those imagined objections, I think. Why haven't you come down here before, Mr.—Mr.——?'

'Tavener,' said Joss gently, his lazy eyes regarding her thoughtfully.

Brown's long lashes flickered for an instant; then she gave a little laugh.

'Oh no—that's too good to be true!' she exclaimed, and Christy sensed Joss's slight withdrawal.

'Coincidence, isn't it?' he said with his slight drawl. 'But my name still happens to be Tavener.'

'Oh, I didn't mean to doubt you,' Brown said hastily, 'but it *is* curious, isn't it? I suppose the very obvious explanation is that you are one of the Tavener relatives Sir Harry has been so anxious to trace.'

'No.'

Christy grinned. She was beginning to know this stranger's method of putting you in your place, at the same time giving out no information, and she was aware, without much sympathy, of the nurse's discomfiture.

'Not? What a strange coincidence. But why didn't you tell us, Christy? The fact that your—er—husband bears the same name would have gone a long way to propitiating Sir Harry.'

Brown stood there, gentle and demure in her familiar crisp overall, her big eyes soft and faintly reproachful in her pale, still face, and Christy was again aware of how little she knew this woman. Brown, her faint smile said, did not believe in coincidence; it had never been really clear whether she had believed the story of the marriage in the first place.

'Where's Gramp? I want to introduce my new husband and get it over with,' Christy said a little defiantly.

Joss put an unexpected arm round her, pulling her towards him.

'You mustn't sound as if you're ashamed of your new husband, my darling,' he said tenderly. But there was no tenderness in his eyes, only the remembered mockery, and the fingers gripping her shoulder were not gentle.

She tried to pull away, but became conscious of Brown's curious gaze, which was at once puzzled and secretive.

'He's in the library. I'll leave you to make your own peace, and I'll bring in the drink-trolley later on,' Brown said, and turned away to disappear directly into one of the downstairs rooms.

'Well,' said Christy, emitting a sigh that was tinged with apprehension, 'now for it! The library means Gramp is sitting in audience. He never uses the room. And you needn't feel obliged to put on the devoted bridegroom act in front of him, Joss. He's not sentimental.'

'Still, he might think complete indifference a little unnatural,' he retorted mildly. 'You haven't, I fear, quite got into the skin of your part, my dear.'

'Shut up! And leave the talking to me, in case you put your foot in it,' she snapped. But she did not altogether care for the expression on his face as she led him across the hall to the library.

It had all gone off surprisingly well, she thought in retrospect. The fact that Sir Harry had established himself in the little-used library rather than his familar untidy study was not lost upon his granddaughter, but to Joss it would have no significance. It was all an act, of course, thought Christy; the old man established in his wheelchair behind a vast desk piled high with the leather-bound tomes which nobody read, peering between his bushy eyebrows and his reading glasses at the door, well aware of the vast expanse of floor that the newcomer must cross before making himself known.

Christy ran across the space lightly, leaving Joss to follow, and dropped a kiss on her grandfather's head.

'Well, here we are, you old tyrant,' she said, perching on the arm of his chair. 'You'll give Joss your blessing, I hope.'

'Joss?' Sir Harry barked the name, glaring at the slowly advancing figure of his new grandson-in-law.

'Josiah—rather sweet, don't you think?'

'No sauce, please, you incorrigible minx. I take it the feller has a surname?'

'Oh yes, darling, and that should soften you up. His name is Tavener.'

'*Tavener!*' The exclamation was the outraged roar of an angry bull, and his beard quivered with indignation as he swept off his glasses to bring Joss into better focus. 'What new prank is this? I've been through the lot of the family offshoots. He'd hardly be the Northumbrian chap, would he?'

'I'm no relation, I'm afraid, Sir Harry, but my name still happens to be Tavener,' Joss said, his voice tinged with amusement. 'How do you do, sir?'

The fierce old eyes travelled over him slowly, and Christy watched, with childish pleasure, her grandfather's belligerent expression changed slowly to one of doubt and perplexity.

'H'm ... not what I expected,' he grunted at last. 'Not what I expected at all.'

'You expected some long-haired artist feller after my money, to quote your own words,' his granddaughter observed sweetly, and he shook her impatiently off the arm of

57

his chair.

'Be quiet!' he snapped. 'Haven't you done enough damage?'

'She's a little headstrong, isn't she?' said Joss. 'But she's young—she'll learn.'

'And you fancy you can teach her?'

'Oh, I think so. I'm sorry, though, that you were kept in ignorance of our marriage. I had, of course, no idea that the child was virtually eloping with me.'

'*Well!*' exclaimed Christy, and he sent her a quick indulgent smile.

'You know you deceived me as well as your grandfather, darling,' he said smoothly. 'But I think we might both forgive her, don't you, Sir Harry? Young girls alone in the world at a tender age often acquire exaggerated romantic notions.'

'The chit was not alone, whatever she may have told you,' Sir Harry barked. 'She's my grandchild, isn't she?'

Joss smiled a little ruefully.

'Well, of course, but—forgive me, sir—I *had* been led to believe you took little or no interest in her. That was rather naughty of you, Christy, wasn't it?'

The old man looked up suddenly and saw the two bright spots of colour on his granddaughter's cheeks and the repressed indignation in her eyes, and gave an unexpected chuckle.

'It seems you've met your match, my girl,' he said. 'But why, in reason's name, couldn't you have told me at the time you had married a Tavener?'

'I—I kept it as a surprise,' she said, fighting down her chagrin. 'Besides, you were in such a rage that evening that you would probably have thought I made it up.'

'I thought you'd made the whole thing up, to tell you the truth,' he retorted, 'but Brown said——'

'What did Brown say, darling?'

'Never you mind. She's a woman, so probably saw

further than I did. Well, young man, I don't mind admitting you're better than I'd hoped for—older, too. But I won't believe that you came by your name by chance. Who were your parents?'

'But he did, Gramp,' said Christy, still smarting from Joss's outrageous insinuations. 'He came by it quite by chance. He was reared in an orphanage and was named after some dirty little creek in the backwoods of Canada.'

'Is that true?'

'Oh yes—in essence,' Joss replied coolly, and Sir Harry shot him a speculative glance.

'H'm...' he said. 'Well, I like you for your honesty. What do you do for a living? Sit down, sit down! This isn't an interview for a prospective job, I trust.'

Joss sat down with leisurely composure and crossed one long leg over the other.

'Well,' he replied, 'at the moment you might say I'm idling. Business brought me over here in the first place, and in due course——'

'Business? What business?'

'—and in due course I shall be returning to Canada,' said Joss, ignoring the interruption.

Sir Harry was instantly diverted.

'Do you imagine you're going to bury my granddaughter abroad when I have my own plans for her?' he shouted, and the other man's eyebrows lifted, the one higher than the other.

'It's usual for a wife to accompany her husband,' he replied, the slight drawl returning. 'And forgive me again, Sir Harry, but your plans for your granddaughter's future seemed a little vague, from what she told me.'

'I suppose you mean Fairmile. Hasn't she made it as plain to you as she has to me that she hopes to inherit? Well, present me with a great-grandson in the course of time, and since he'll be a Tavener at least in name, you may yet find yourselves here when I'm gone.'

Christy began fidgeting uneasily with the pile of books on the desk, dry-as-dust tomes intended to impress the interloper which, together with the vast, gloomy and rather musty apartment and Sir Harry's obvious trappings of authority, had clearly failed to intimidate Joss.

'Personally, Sir Harry,' she heard him answer mildly, 'I shouldn't care to make my home here. My roots are in Canada.'

'What!' the old man exploded. 'You'd turn down Fairmile for some benighted shack in the backwoods? You'll not do my only grandchild and her sons out of their inheritance for some tomfool notion of your own, let me tell you.'

'This would seem to be a subject I'm not prepared to discuss at present—and it's not necessary to live in a benighted shack in the backwoods, you know,' Joss said gently, and Christy's wide mouth curved up in an appreciative grin. Clever ... clever ... she thought. Nothing, she knew, made Gramp more determined on a set course than opposition, but she caught Joss's sardonic eye upon her for an instant and felt less confident.

'Darling,' she said hastily, sliding an arm round her grandfather's shoulders, 'let's not talk of such things now. This should be a welcome-home occasion for the erring grandchild and her—her bridegroom. Where's the famous Tavener hospitality?'

'True for you, monkey. Where's that drink-trolley? Ring the bell,' Sir Harry said and, as if on cue, Rose Brown came into the room pushing the trolley. Besides the usual array of bottles there was an ice-packed bucket holding a magnum of champagne, and Christy clapped her hands like a child.

'Bubbly!' she cried. 'Beautiful, sparkling, high-class bubbly! Now I know you've forgiven me, Gramp—you only bring out the champagne on very special occasions.'

'Don't you be too sure, young woman. This stuff wants drinking anyhow; it's getting past its prime,' the old man grunted. 'Here, bring the trolley nearer, Brown, so I can get at it.'

'Shall I open it for you, sir?' Joss asked, and the old man shot him an appraising look.

'Think you can?'

'Oh, I'm quite civilized,' Joss replied, and proceeded to deal very expertly with the champagne. A toast was given and drunk, and when the glasses were filled again, Joss raised his to Christy and said:

'May I drink a special toast to my charming bride? I haven't got around to it yet, except in beer,' he said, and Sir Harry chuckled.

'Hard pressed for the ready, were you?' he said. 'Well, you won't have to bother about that as long as you're stopping at Fairmile. What did you say your business was?'

'I didn't. We will, no doubt, be having the usual talk later on, Sir Harry?'

'Quite right, quite right—only bore the ladies, what? My little granddaughter's shown more sense than we gave her credit for, I'm beginning to think, eh, Brown?'

The nurse murmured something non-committal and stood sipping her champagne, her eyes gazing thoughtfully from one to the other of them.

'What part of Canada are you from, Mr. Tavener?' Brown asked in her soft voice, and was unaware that she had been appraising his appearance with scarcely concealed curiosity until she caught the little quirk of amusement at the corner of his mouth.

'Oh, I move around. My contacts take me to various places,' he replied evasively, and, whatever his intention, she took it as a snub.

'I'm sorry, I was merely interested,' she said a little stiffly, and was surprised, as Christy had been, at the alteration the sudden smile made to his face.

'Well now, I'm sure you'd both like to see your room,' she said briskly. 'I've put you in the famous bridal chamber, of course, Christy.'

61

Christy's hand flew in a childish gesture to her mouth, and her eyes met the nurse's with a hint of panic.

'We can't sleep there—it only has one *bed*!' she exclaimed, and Brown's eyebrows rose.

'Well, it's big enough in all conscience,' she retorted. 'You might have remembered, Christy, that Fairmile has never adopted the twin bed habit.'

'But we must have separate *rooms*!' Christy protested. 'I never thought—I mean, I *should* have thought——'

'What should you have thought?' Brown asked gently, and her eyes narrowed a fraction.

'Never mind what she thought,' Sir Harry interrupted irritably. 'I've no patience with these new-fangled fads. Separate rooms, forsooth! What did you want to get married for, I should like to know? Do you share these modern notions too, young feller?'

'Oh, *I* have no objections,' Joss said lazily. 'Where I come from the good old double bed is a mark of respectability.'

'Good! Then you'll doubtless knock some sense into this pert young miss who thinks she knows all the answers.'

'*Joss!*' Christy wailed, as it dawned on her that he was not prepared to help her out.

For a long moment he kept her in suspense, while his eyes, lazy and mocking, dwelt speculatively on her flushed face. Then he said to Sir Harry with a hint of resignation:

'I'm afraid we do find it more harmonious to occupy separate rooms, sir. You see, she snores.'

'*Oh!*' cried Christy wrathfully. 'I've never snored in my life!'

'Darling, you do,' he said with indulgent rebuke. 'Don't you remember that night when even the couple in the next room were banging on the wall?'

Brown turned away, hiding a smile.

'Then you'd better have the little suite in the west wing. You can close the door between the adjoining rooms if necessary,' she said. 'I'll go and tell Mrs. Heap.'

'Stuff and nonsense!' muttered Sir Harry crossly. 'Take her to a specialist, m'boy—probably got adenoids.'

'I have not, then! They were taken out when I was a child,' Christy retorted, and for a moment looked very near tears.

'Probably grown again, and that's why you sleep with your mouth open,' observed Joss unkindly, and she turned her back on him.

To make her displeasure plain, she began making a fuss of her grandfather, wheedling smiles from him, teasing and conciliatory by turn, shutting the stranger out; but when Brown came back to say the fresh rooms were ready, she could do no less than take Joss upstairs. She preserved an icy silence as she led the way round the gallery and along a corridor to the west wing, but when the door of their little suite had closed behind them, she turned on him fiercely.

'Of all the mean tricks!' she exclaimed. 'It was bad enough not to back me up about the bridal chamber, but to make the excuse that I *snored*——!'

'Well, I had to think of something, since you had so obviously forgotten that a newly married couple might be expected to share a room,' he retorted. 'And for all I know, you *may* snore.'

'Don't be such a beast!' she cried, and he surprised her by taking her by the shoulders and turning her gently round to face him.

'You really are an absurd child,' he said. 'Did it never occur to you that you might be letting yourself in for more than you'd bargained when you suggested this crazy charade?'

She looked up at him uncertainly, aware that this was the first time he had touched her, except for that brief moment of play-acting in the hall, and what she saw in his face silenced the childish insults hovering on her lips. He no longer seemed the casual out-of-work stranger willing to pick up a little easy money, and she became uneasily aware that the impersonal balance of their relationship during the next week or so lay in his hands and not in hers.

'Why should I?' she replied, as he seemed to be waiting for an answer. 'I made it plain that our arrangement was strictly business.'

'So you did,' he said, 'but wasn't that rather trusting of you?'

'What do you mean?'

'You know very well what I mean. I don't imagine you're so naïve as to be blind to your own attractions.'

'Naturally not. Are you trying to make a pass?'

He let her go then, rather abruptly, as if the subject had become distasteful.

'Oh no,' he said. 'Time enough for that, should conditions become more propitious. You have quite a conceit of yourself, haven't you?'

'I don't think so, but I've been around,' she replied quite seriously, and the hard, rather sardonic expression on his face vanished in a smile.

'I was forgetting,' he said. 'Miss Christobel Tavener, comfortably cushioned against life's importunities, and knowing most of the answers. Which room do you want for yourself? We should be getting unpacked.'

'Someone's done it already—Brown, I expect. My things are in this room,' she said, feeling her colour rise, and watched him stroll through the open door to inspect the adjoining room.

'Very nice, very romantic. There's no key in the lock,' he observed, and her self-confidence returned.

'It's quite simple to wedge a chair under the door-knob,' she retorted.

'True—but won't that look rather odd to whoever calls us in the morning?'

'I don't care how odd it looks. Brown usually brings the

64

early tea, anyway. We're very short-staffed these days.'

'Oh? You might be unwise to give Nurse Brown further food for thought,' he remarked casually.

'What do you mean?'

'Just a vague notion—probably quite misplaced.'

He stood in the doorway, contemplating her dispassionately for a moment.

'Don't worry, Christobel, you're quite safe from me,' he said.

'Why?' she demanded, feeling affronted.

'Not my type, I expect,' he replied, and shut the door between them.

CHAPTER FOUR

As Christy had predicted, Brown brought up the morning tea. The tray was laid for one, with the familiar Minton china and thin bread and butter.

'Doesn't Joss get any?' Christy asked, yawning as she struggled up against her pillows. She had slept badly, conscious that the door between their rooms had been firmly shut by him with an absent-minded good night, and saw, out of the tail of her eye, that the door now stood open.

'Mr. Tavener is already up,' Brown replied demurely, and her manner seemed to convey that Christy should have known.

'Oh! What's he doing at this unearthly hour?'

'I've no idea, but it's a fine morning—he's probably inspecting the grounds. He's hardly the pampered type, would you say?'

Christy frowned as she poured out the tea.

'What do you mean, pampered?' she asked, and the nurse gave a little shrug.

'Well—early morning tea, the little comforts of an age that boasted servants.'

Christy glanced at her quickly, wondering if she detected an unsuspected resentment.

'You don't *need* to bring up early tea, do you, Brownie? Not to me, anyway,' she said apologetically, and Brown smiled.

'I don't mind,' she said. 'Why should I? After all, I'm paid handsomely for my services.'

Christy sipped her tea in silence. There was, after all, no reason to suppose that Brown was discontented, and even if she was, the remedy was in her own hands.

'You wouldn't leave Gramp, would you?' Christy asked,

digesting this thought, and the nurse raised her eyebrows.

'Now why should you ask that?' she said. 'I'm devoted to your grandfather, as you ought to know—besides, when you go to Canada, he will be more than ever dependent on me.'

'Why on earth should I go to Canada?' Christy exclaimed, spilling tea on the sheet in her astonishment, and Brown smiled, that little secret smile which seemed to match the hidden thoughts in her eyes.

'Well, you'll be returning with your husband in due course, I imagine,' she said, and Christy felt she had been caught out.

'Oh, yes, of course,' she replied vaguely, and saw the nurse give another little smile. She glanced at the open door, wondering if Joss had stood there, watching as she slept, and knew at once that he must have opened it when he was dressed to satisfy the curiosity of whoever should bring up the morning tea.

'How's Gramp?' she asked with forced flippancy. 'None the worse for the shock of meeting his new grandson-in-law, I hope?'

'On the contrary. Mr. Tavener, I suspect, will prove to be a man after Sir Harry's own heart. You've been clever, haven't you, Christy?' Brown said lightly.

'Clever?' The old doubt as to whether the nurse had really believed her story in the first place returned. 'Brown, you were never sure, were you?'

'Sure of what?'

'Whether I'd invented the whole thing. I mean, you practically suggested that solution yourself.'

Brown began moving about the room, automatically straightening things, picking up garments thrown carelessly on the floor, managing to suggest both rebuke and resignation by her actions.

'You really should take more care of your things, Christy,' she said. 'It's easy to see you haven't had to count the cost of a new dress. What solution are you talking about, and to what problem?'

'You know perfectly well. The last time I was here, I had a showdown with Gramp, and——'

'The last time you were here, you and I talked a lot of nonsense, I've no doubt,' Brown interrupted calmly. 'I was hardly to know that any idle suggestion of mine was already a fact, was I? I'm very happy for you, Christy. Mr. Tavener would appear to be just what you need.'

'What do you mean?'

'Well, he's older and experienced in the matter of feminine vagaries, I would say.'

'How do you know?'

'Oh, I've been around too,' Brown said sweetly. 'Funny his name should be Tavener, isn't it?'

Christy bounced impatiently in the bed, spilling the tea again.

'What are you getting at?' she asked uneasily.

'Nothing. It's not my place to criticize or offer opinions. I just take things at face value.'

'Do you? But you must have natural curiosity. You haven't even asked me when I was married.'

'Does it matter? The fact that you *are* married will have satisfied your grandfather that you can't be expected to make your home here, won't it?' said Brown gently, and went out of the room.

Christy dressed quickly, pulling on the familiar jeans and shirt, screwing her hair into its accustomed pony-tail, dabbing on powder and lipstick with scant regard for artistic result, concerned only that on this first day she should have been doing the honours of Fairmile and Joss had beaten her to it.

She ran through the house and down the stairs and out into the warm promise of a September morning. Dew still shimmered on the grass and the leaves had scarcely begun to turn.

She came upon the old swing hung between two apple trees which, in high summer, could swing one over a meadow lush with cowslips and buttercups. Someone had pushed her, she remembered, high over the grass so that she could almost snatch the fruit from the branches above her head. So much change since that time, she thought, so many new experiences for a child brought up in foreign places. She moved towards the swing with an instinctive desire to recapture the lost delights of an English childhood.

The old swing creaked as she sat in it, and the ropes felt harsh and stiff to her hands, but the half-remembered ecstasy returned as she started swinging. The meadow dipped and curved beneath her, and now she could reach out for the fruit which hung above her head. Out of the corner of her eye she saw Joss's tall figure strolling back from the derelict outbuildings, but he had no part with her then. She was a child again, swinging high, swinging low, supreme in her solitude above the earth.

He stood watching her, thinking that she had not seen him. The ribbon had slipped from her hair and it flew out behind her in a flaxen cloud. Her young body arched and curved to the rhythm of the swing's movements and she kicked off a sandal that was hanging loosely from one foot.

Even as he watched, there was a rending sound, a rope, rotten with the years, broke and the swing tipped sideways, throwing her on to the grass. For a moment she lay there without moving, and he leapt the sunken fence which divided them and knelt beside her.

'Christy, are you all right?' he asked sharply, and added, as she tried to sit up: 'Don't move for a moment.'

She felt his hands run over her limbs, firm, assured hands, the rough callouses rasping her flesh. When he was satisfied that her hurts would amount to no more than bruises, he got to his feet, pulling her with him. One leg gave under her for a moment and he held her close in support. The lean, dark face touched her hair and she could see the tiny lines at the corners of his eyes and the small nerve that jerked, surprisingly, at the side of his mouth. She looked up at him, diverted between the pain in her foot and the unexpected concern she read in his face.

'I scared you, didn't I?' she said, and saw at once a return of the familiar hard-bitten expression of indifference.

'Naturally you scared me,' he retorted. 'You could have broken a leg or an arm, and then where would we have been, with you laid up and your doting grandpapa expecting the devoted bridegroom to stop on indefinitely?'

'Yes, of course. Well, you needn't worry. I'm no more anxious to prolong the visit than you are. A week or so and then we can make our excuses,' she replied coldly.

'And what excuses do you imagine your by no means gullible grandparent is going to accept for his new-found relative by marriage vanishing into thin air?'

'H'm . . . I hadn't thought of that.'

'You hadn't thought of very much beyond the needs of the moment, had you?'

'I suppose not. Still'— she brightened visibly—'you can always have urgent business recalling you to Canada and I, of course, would be expected to accompany you.'

'Good grief!'

'Naturally I shouldn't, so don't go up in the air! I've plenty of friends in other places abroad. After a decent interval we would notify Gramp from some distant country that things hadn't worked out and we'd got a divorce. It's done every day.'

'Is it indeed?' His voice was suddenly a little grim. 'And am I supposed to be the scapegoat in this charming little plot—the convenient rolling-stone from Canada disappeared without trace?'

She was still standing between his hands, but neither of them seemed aware of it. The clear hazel eyes she raised to his were grave and innocent and suddenly cool.

70

'Is it much to expect for five hundred pounds?' she said. 'You knew the terms when you accepted my proposition.'

He let her go then with such suddenness that she sat down ignominiously at his feet.

'I doubt if you'd thought overmuch about the consequences,' he retorted with a bite to his voice. 'Well, Christy, I'll play ball for a time, but things may not work out as you planned. I don't know that I very much care about deceiving your grandfather, now that I've met him.'

'Why? You've done worse than that in your chequered career, I don't mind betting!'

'You'd lose your bet on a great many of the opinions you've formed about me, Christobel,' he replied with deceptive mildness. 'You're a spoilt brat, my dear—a spoilt brat whom it would give me much pleasure to spank.'

'You wouldn't dare!' she cried. 'And please help me up, since you threw me down here.'

'I wouldn't be bothered with a spanking,' he retorted unkindly. 'And you're quite able to get up by yourself. I'm going in to breakfast.'

Breakfast was made no easier by the presence of Rose Brown, who, judging by her curious glances and bright attempts to keep the conversation from flagging, suspected a lovers' tiff.

'You were up early, Mr. Tavener,' she volunteered, looking up at him under her lashes. 'Christy was quite surprised to find you gone when I brought up the tea.'

'Christy knows very well I'm an early riser. You probably mistook surprise for relief,' he replied, and her lashes veiled her eyes.

'Oh! What an odd thing to say.'

'Not really. One's scarcely at one's best in the early morning and women like time to scrape off all that muck they put on at night.'

She sent him a quick look which implied that she did not take him seriously and said, with an affectionate glance at the girl's young, tender skin:

'I don't think Christy needs to trouble much about face-creams yet. By the way, don't you wear your engagement ring?'

Christy looked guiltily down at the plain platinum circle which still felt strange on her finger and said quickly:

'I'm afraid of losing it.' She should, of course, have thought of something that would pass as an engagement ring.

'What is it?'

'Er—a sapphire,' she replied vaguely, and Joss observed with a blatant wink:

'Come off it, darling! You know I couldn't afford a ring. However, when times are better, of course——' He left the sentence carelessly in mid-air and the nurse gave Christy a wry little smile of commiseration.

'Well, a wedding ring's rather more important, isn't it?' she said brightly. 'And Christy will have her mother's jewellery to make up. Aren't you eating, my dear?'

'Not hungry,' said Christy.

'Probably slimming. She knows I can't stand plump women,' said Joss, and Christy got up from the table and slammed out of the room.

'Why do you tease?' Brown asked with gentle reproach. 'The child takes these things seriously.'

'Then it's time she learnt to laugh at herself, don't you think?' Joss observed mildly, and she smiled.

'I imagine when one is in love and first married it isn't easy to laugh at oneself,' she said.

'Possibly not—still, there's no need to embarrass people by parading one's affection at every turn, is there?'

She buttered a piece of toast thoughtfully, then poured herself a second cup of coffee with the neat, deliberate movements which seemed characteristic of her.

'You're a strange man, Mr. Tavener,' she said. 'I've only just met you of course, but you don't strike me as the typical fortune-hunter.'

'Thanks very much,' he replied. 'Is that Sir Harry's opinion of me, or merely yours?'

'Forgive me,' she murmured, with a small, conciliatory smile. 'No, Sir Harry likes you—that's what's a little puzzling.'

'Why? Am I so unlikeable?'

'You persist in misunderstanding me. I only meant that when Christy sprang this sudden marriage on us, we both, naturally, had doubts. Where did you meet and when were you married?'

His eyes were still lazy as they dwelt casually on her pale, composed face, but one eyebrow lifted a fraction.

'Hasn't Sir Harry told you?' he asked, and for a moment she looked nonplussed.

'He said nothing while I was helping him to dress,' she replied a little shortly.

'Ah well, perhaps he doesn't confide everything. You have a rather personal concern for your patient, I think, Nurse Brown.'

'I don't understand you. Naturally I'm personally concerned. Sir Harry has been good to me.' For the first time she sounded a little ruffled, and Joss pushed back his chair and got up.

'Naturally,' he said. 'Had you been here long before Christy came home?'

'A year or so.'

'Yes, I see. It must have been a little unexpected when the prodigal granddaughter returned to take her place as mistress of the house.'

'There was scarcely any question of that,' the nurse replied tranquilly. 'Christy didn't care to make her home here for any length of time.'

'But the old man hoped?'

'Sir Harry is very fond of his granddaughter, but now that she is married, the question, of course, doesn't arise.'

'And naturally you will stop on and take her place.'

'I will stop, of course, as long as I'm needed.' He stood looking reflectively down on her and she gave him a serene little smile. 'What are you thinking, Mr. Tavener?'

'I was, in fact, wondering why you haven't told me long ago to mind my own business and stop asking impertinent questions. You are a very interesting woman, Nurse Brown,' he said, and saw the two unaccustomed spots of colour fly to her cheeks as he left her sitting at the table, and went out of the room.

The first days of the visit slipped so easily one into another that it was with a feeling of surprise that Christy realized that they had been there a week, and then a fortnight, and already Joss had become part of the familiar background, and there was no urge to move on. Sir Harry seemed to have taken to the idea of the marriage as wholeheartedly as he had opposed it, and only Rose Brown appeared to have reservations which might or might not be due to what she considered a seemly attitude.

'Don't you like him?' Christy asked her, wondering idly what tastes Brown might have in the matter of men, and the nurse replied, with a faint smile:

'I hardly know him. In any case, my personal opinion can scarcely matter, can it?'

'Of course it matters, dear Brownie. You're almost one of the family, after all. Does Gramp talk to you about Joss?'

'You're very curious, Christy. I should have thought it was fairly obvious that your grandfather has—accepted your husband.'

'Yes, it's all been too easy, hasn't it?'

'Too easy? What an odd thing to say.'

'I—I meant knowing how stubborn he can be. I—we had expected more opposition.'

Brown looked at her thoughtfully.

'You should be grateful things have turned out as they

have,' she said. 'You *might* have found yourself cut out of his will altogether by this sort of defiance. As it is—well, I should be careful if I were you.'

'What do you mean?'

'Nothing, probably, but Sir Harry wouldn't take kindly to finding himself deceived.'

Christy frowned, uneasily aware that the nurse seemed fond of talking in riddles.

'My affairs are my own concern,' she said with sudden coolness. 'Were you hinting at something, Brown?'

Brown's lashes hid her eyes in two demure crescents.

'Of course not,' she replied serenely. 'As you yourself are hinting, my dear, it's not my place to speculate—or criticize.'

The girl's mouth curved into that sudden disarming grin.

'Don't be prickly, Brownie dear,' she said affectionately. 'Why shouldn't you have your opinions? Anyway, we don't, either of us, know what's in Gramp's will, do we?'

Brown smiled back automatically and left the room without replying.

If Christy knew a passing disquiet on these occasions it was soon forgotten in the pleasure of introducing her favourite haunts to Joss, showing off a little to impress him with Fairmile's worth and her own good fortune until, quite good-naturedly, he would slap her down, calling her a spoilt brat. Even then she would boast a little more with innocent solemnity, or hurl childish abuse at him which only made him laugh.

'I was right,' he would say. 'This sudden independence has gone to your head. You think money can buy most things, don't you?'

'And so it can,' she would retort, and then turn suddenly humble.

'Do you really think I'm a spoilt brat, Joss?'

'Would you care if I did?'

'Yes, I think so.'

His dark eyebrows rose in sceptical surprise.

'Out of character,' he replied with his slight drawl. 'Miss Christobel Tavener cares little for any man, to say nothing of a down-at-heel stranger hired for convenience.'

'You don't *look* down-at-heel,' she said, eyeing his well-cut tweeds suspiciously. 'You seem, in fact, to have quite a wardrobe.'

'Well, I hope you think your two hundred and fifty was well spent.'

'Your clothes aren't new,' she said shrewdly, and he grinned at her with irritating mockery.

'You're becoming observant, Christobel. Watch out you don't cut yourself with your own sharpness, as my nanny used to say.'

'You never had a nanny! You told me yourself you were raised in an orphanage.'

'Only until the age of seven. After that I had a nanny like other well-brought-up little boys.'

She forgot her perpetual desire to bicker with him in surprised curiosity.

'Did someone adopt you?' she asked. 'Are you a kind of male Cinderella, fairy godmother and all?'

'Fairy godfather, if you want to be exact,' he replied, and there was a hint of provocation in his suddenly lazy eyes. 'But the pumpkin scarcely turned into a fairy coach. He was a mean old codger and something of an eccentric. He kept tame snakes in his bedroom.'

'I don't believe a word of it!' she exclaimed indignantly, then gave him a sidelong glance which was suddenly tender.

'I expect you were sent out as hired labour to a cattle ranch or something as soon as you were old enough to earn. Isn't that usually what happens to orphans?'

'If you prefer that version. You seem to have made up your mind that I'm a rolling stone—a kind of hobo. I wonder why.'

'Your hands,' she said. 'It's plain you've worked with

76

your hands.'

They were strolling across the deserted stable yard on their way to look at the old drag in the coach-house, and Joss held out his hands, inspecting the callouses and hard, roughened skin.

'Very observant,' he said again, this time a little dryly. 'It didn't occur to you, I suppose, that messing about with boats can upset the best of manicures? One doesn't just sit back and clap one's hands for minions to appear to do the dirty jobs.'

'Oh!' She remembered that of course he had crewed for the owner of the cabin cruiser, which had put into the harbour at St. Bede, and wondered if she had been presuming altogether too much about him.

'I didn't mean to be impertinent,' she said a little shyly, and he looked surprised.

'Didn't you? Well, Christy, it's nice to know you can have flashes of humility, despite your great wealth.'

She gave him another sidelong glance, caught the unexpected twinkle in his eye, and grinned.

'You shouldn't laugh at me, and I'm not as rich as all that,' she said.

'Why shouldn't I laugh at you?'

'Because it's disrespectful to a temporary employer. When our—our contract is finished, you can laugh to your heart's content.'

'I may take you up on that,' he retorted, and she looked up, puzzled by the note of gravity in his voice, but the mockery was still there in his eyes and she ran ahead of him into the coach-house, feeling disconcerted.

'Isn't this a splendid equipage?' she said, pointing to the drag and talking rather fast. 'I used to hide in it when I was little and play at highwaymen with the chauffeur's son. Do you know that my mother could remember driving to church in it when she was a very little girl? She said it used to be one of the famous sights of the district, like the chestnut avenue. It was ages before Gramp took to a car.'

She tugged at one of the brass door handles and, scrambling inside, bounced on the ancient springs, sending up a cloud of dust. Joss stood and watched her, smiling with sudden indulgence as she peered at him out of the gloom. The fair hair fell forward over her bare, tanned shoulders above a strapless sun-frock, and there was a streak of dirt on one cheekbone.

'Come inside with me,' she invited, and he obligingly climbed in beside her.

It smelt very damp and musty, and mice had made nests in the stuffing of the seats. Christy's face was suddenly close to his and she rubbed one bare shoulder against his, pleased as any child playing at make-believe. He took her chin in one hand and turned her face gently towards him.

'A good place for a tryst as well as for children's games, perhaps,' he said, and smiled as he saw her eyes widen. 'No, I'm not going to kiss you. Is that what you were expecting?'

'Possibly,' she answered calmly, but her colour rose. 'After all, I'm reasonably attractive. Oh, of course. I remember you said I wasn't your type.'

His smile was quite kindly.

'Did that sting? You are a little obvious, my dear.'

'I didn't bring you here for that!' she said, trying to pull away from him. 'You're hateful ... hateful! I thought you'd understand. . . .'

'Good grief!' he exclaimed softly, seeing the tears bright on her lashes. 'Of course I understood.'

'Then why do you suddenly turn it into something cheap and shoddy?'

'Why do you take it for granted that a man will make a pass at you with the slightest provocation, and then feel slighted if he doesn't?' he countered gently, and her head drooped a little wearily against his shoulder.

'I don't as a rule, but *they* do, and—and I don't think I

understand you very well, Joss,' she said, and felt the harsh skin of his fingers as he brushed them across her wet lashes.

'No, I don't think you do,' he replied. 'Come on—we'd better get back to the house. It must be nearly lunch-time.'

He got out of the drag and reached up to lift her down. Holding her with one hand he produced a clean pocket-handkerchief with the other and bade her spit.

'Nursery drill. Your face is dirty,' he said, and proceeded to clean her up.

'Did you really have a nanny?' she asked irrelevantly as they walked out into the sunlight.

'Yes, I really did,' he answered with faint amusement, and began to whistle. He whistled well, soft, pure notes like a bird's, and always, it seemed, the same elusive, rather melancholy little air. Christy was just going to ask him what it was when they saw Rose Brown hurrying towards them across the stable yard.

'I've been looking for you everywhere,' she said. 'Didn't you hear me calling? Your grandfather's had another slight attack. The doctor has just gone.'

Christy went white.

'A real attack, or is he foxing?' she said sharply, and started to run as the nurse shook her head, but Brown called her back.

'It's Mr. Tavener he wants to see, not you, my dear,' she said. Her eyes were more curious than sympathetic as they rested on the girl's alarmed face, seeing only the ruffled hair and faint air of dishevelment which, she thought, told their own story of the morning's activities. 'Will you go at once, please, Mr. Tavener? We've put him to bed and you know where his room is by now.'

'But I must go, too,' Christy cried, and Joss's sudden grip on her shoulder was firm and none too gentle.

'Stay with Nurse Brown. If you're wanted I'll fetch you,' he said curtly, and walked quickly away to the house.

Luncheon was an uncomfortable meal. Joss appeared to be sharing Sir Harry's tray in his bedroom, and Christy and Brown were left in uneasy solitude.

'What brought on the attack?' Christy asked, picking indifferently at her food.

'You'd been talking of leaving, I think,' the nurse replied, and Christy frowned. She had made no mention of their departure, because, perhaps, the thought had not occurred to her with the easy passage of time, but possibly Joss . . .

'We only came for a week or so,' she said lamely, and was aware of Brown's veiled attentiveness.

'Yes—well, of course *I* understand you have your own lives to lead,' Brown replied. 'But Sir Harry is an old man and clings to what he knows.'

'He didn't know Joss until a fortnight ago. He hasn't, for the matter of that, known *me* for very long,' Christy retorted. The nurse smiled.

'You don't need to feel guilty, my dear,' she said. 'I was sufficient company for your grandfather before you came and I've no doubt I'll be sufficient when you've gone. Eat something, Christy—there's no need for alarm at present.'

Christy pushed away her plate impatiently. Was there a hidden threat in Brown's soft reply, or had she merely beeen trying to put matters on a sensible basis?

'Why did he want to see Joss—why not me?' she asked, and, for an instant, the other woman's flash of uncertainty matched her own.

'I don't know,' she said slowly. 'They talk together and it's plain that, whatever the truth of the matter, Sir Harry accepts your husband as a Tavener.'

'What do you mean—the truth of the matter?' Christy sounded on the defensive, and the nurse merely raised her eyebrows and smiled.

'Didn't you both say the name was only his by adoption?' she replied gently. 'Your grandfather, I imagine, considers the coincidence too much of a good thing and prefers to regard your husband as a blood-relation of sorts.'

'And you, Brown?'

'I? Well, there's only one other conclusion, isn't there? You made the whole thing up.'

'What do you mean?'

'The name, of course. Knowing Sir Harry's fixation, it would be quite clever to call yourselves Tavener and soften the shock of your sudden marriage, wouldn't it? Don't think *I* would blame you, Christy dear—what name you were married in and what you choose to call yourselves here is no concern of mine. When will you be returning to Canada?'

'You'd better ask my husband,' Christy snapped, her eyes defiant and very bright, and Joss walked into the room.

'What should Nurse Brown ask me?' he inquired, regarding them both with a quizzical expression, and smiled faintly when Christy thumped two clenched fists on the table like a thwarted child.

'She wants to know when we're returning to Canada,' she said as Joss turned to look at the nurse with a reflective eye.

'Well, now,' he said conversationally, 'that's a question I haven't considered yet. What makes you so sure I don't intend to settle in England?'

For the first time Brown looked disconcerted.

'Well, I suppose I took it for granted,' she said, colouring slightly. 'It was only a casual and quite natural inquiry on my part, Mr. Tavener. I didn't mean to be impertinent.'

'I'm sure you didn't,' he replied courteously. 'But you shouldn't take things for granted, Nurse—it can be a great mistake!'

Two faint spots of colour stained the nurse's cheeks, but, if she recognized the polite snub, she refused to accept it.

'There are many things that can be a mistake, Mr. Tavener. We are all human, I think you'll agree,' she said, and

Christy watched with sudden interest the provocative tilt of Brown's head as she looked up at Joss, and the veiled and fleeting invitation in her eyes. Why, she's flirting with him! she thought, completely diverted for the moment, then experienced a most unfamiliar reaction as she saw the amused comprehension on Joss's face.

'Isn't it time my grandfather asked for *me*?' she demanded truculently. 'You might reassure us, Joss, instead of—instead of——'

'Instead of what?' he replied with irritating calm. 'You can go and see him now, if you like. I'm sure Nurse Brown has already explained that there's no cause for alarm.'

'But he asked for *you*—you who are a stranger—and a doubtful one at that!'

'Dear me! What a way to talk to your husband,' Joss said with a reproving shake of the head. But there was a hint of warning in his voice. 'Run along and satisfy yourself that I haven't replaced you in his affections. We were merely talking business.'

'Business? What business could you have with Gramp?'

'Well, there are natural adjustments to be made when fresh blood comes into the family. You'd better ask him yourself, my dear.'

She ran out of the room, glad to get away from them both. Between them, Joss and Brown succeeded in making her feel like a tiresome child; she wanted her grandfather's reassurance, and the familiar bickering between them which, unlike that which she was forced into with Joss, left her feeling she was adult and feminine.

'Darling!' she cried, flinging herself down beside the bed. 'Are you really all right? Why didn't you send for me? What did you want with Joss? What did the doctor say? Do you know what a fright you've given us?'

'Hey, one thing at a time!' Sir Harry protested, submitting rather peevishly to her demonstrations of affection. The fierce, still youthful eyes were as bright as ever, and the well-cleared dishes on his discarded luncheon tray bore evidence that his appetite was still excellent.

'You old humbug!' she scolded. 'I believe you were foxing after all—like the time you wrote me pathetic letters to get me to come home.'

'Well, I succeeded, didn't I?' he retorted. 'You'd have cheated me out of meeting my grandson-in-law otherwise.'

'You didn't want to meet him. You didn't want to have anything to do with him—or me—last time I was here.'

'But you came.'

He closed his eyes and for a moment he looked tired and old and what he was, the handsome wreck of a man who had lived his life too well and been denied in the end his dearest wish. Pity born of a new maturity touched Christy's young face with fleeting beauty, and her hands were gentle on his.

'I couldn't take a chance on whether you were having me on or not, could I? I love you very much, Gramp,' she said softly, and his wrinkled eyelids lifted.

'H'm . . .' he grunted. 'Me or Fairmile?'

'To hell with Fairmile!' she exclaimed impatiently. 'You are my flesh and blood.'

'I believe you mean that—pity you weren't a boy. Still, you can change that now for me, can't you?'

'What do you mean?' she faltered, and he winked at her blatantly.

'You know very well, monkey. All this nonsense about separate rooms and such-like modern balderdash! You've got a decent man, Christy—better than I'd given you credit for. I like the chap; won't stand the backchat I have to take from you, either, I don't mind betting. Feller of substance, too. More than I'd hoped for with a chit like you dangling your money and supposed expectations in front of the greedy eyes of every Tom, Dick and Harry. . . .' He tailed off, sounding suddenly sleepy, and Christy had difficulty in refraining from blurting out the whole sorry story. How dared Joss lead the old man up the garden, pretending to a background he did not possess? How dared he, for the matter of that, worm his way into a person's affections when, his five hundred pounds safely earned, he would disappear from their lives and never be heard of again?

'Joss hasn't any money—at least let me be honest about that, Gramp,' she said, but he closed his eyes again.

'What are you talking about? Go away, m'dear, and let me sleep. I'm tired, and my head aches. Tell Brown to come and sit with me.'

'Brown? I'll sit with you while you sleep,' she said, trying in some small measure to make amends, but he gave a drowsy chuckle and turned over in his bed with his back to her.

'Not the same thing,' he said. 'Brown flatters my ego. Damn fine woman, Brown ... knows her onions ... might oblige her yet with a title if it makes her happy. Run away, my girl....'

She went back to the dining-room, angry and disturbed and dimly afraid. Brown was no longer there, but Joss still sat at the deserted luncheon table, idly flicking pellets of bread across the polished surface. Christy gleefully and without further thought set about picking a quarrel with him.

'What have you been up to with Gramp?' she demanded, and he flicked another pellet across the table without bothering to look at her.

'*Now* what's the trouble?' he asked, but did not sound very interested.

'Leading him up the garden—letting him think you're a man of substance, when all the time you're a—you're a——'

'Well, what am I?'

'A layabout—a—a tramp taking easy money from a girl! If he knew the truth——'

'If he knew the truth, do you imagine you'd be in much

84

of a position, yourself, to fling mud around?' he asked quite mildly, then, with a suddenness that took her by surprise, sprang to his feet and grasped her by the shoulders.

'I'll take so much from you, Christy, since I appear to be in your debt, but layabout, tramp—I could think of harsher words to apply to you.'

She stared up at him, not at all liking the expression on his dark face, but she was still ready to do battle.

'I've no doubt your vocabulary is rich in rude epithets,' she retorted. 'But the fact remains that you took on my proposition with your eyes open, so what have you to complain of?'

'I doubt if you'd understand my complaints,' he said, giving her a shake. 'It's the old story, my dear; money can buy anything—but you won't buy me, for all that.'

'I hired you, didn't I?' she said, and he let her go as suddenly as he had seized her, and turned away towards the window, seeming all at once indifferent and relaxed.

'Yes, you hired me,' he said. 'But that doesn't give you rights over me. What, after all, do you know about me? What have you ever troubled to find out?'

'Why should I trouble to find out anything? When we leave here, we're not likely to meet again.'

'True—but in the meantime we each have a part to play. Your grandfather is a sick man, you know.'

The anger drained out of her. However hostile he might appear, she still wanted assurance that Gramp was only foxing.

'How sick?' she asked, and at the humble, pleading note in her voice, he turned to look at her with unexpected kindness.

'Well, not mortally, as far as we know,' he said. 'But he's old and choleric and has lived his life too well. Heart attacks, however slight, can't be ignored at his age. Do you really care about him?'

'You know I do.'

'Yes, I think I do. Well, you started this, Christy—you'll have to play it out to the end.'

'And what is the end?'

The softness went from his face and the old, hard-bitten expression returned.

'That's your worry, isn't it?' he said, the slight Canadian accent lending his speech the familiar drawl. 'Myself, I should say we'd been here long enough. A week or two, you told me at the beginning. It's getting on for three.'

Yes, it was, she thought with surprise, observing through the window how deeply the leaves had turned in the parkland, conscious that the strapless sun-frock she wore was already out of season.

'We can't go till Gramp is better,' she said, and shivered a little.

'Naturall, but that won't be long, and there's always Nurse Brown to take over.'

'Brown? Oh, of course. Joss—would you think Brown was *up* to something?'

He smiled. She was very naïve in the ease with which she could switch from aggression to confiding ingenuousness.

'I think Nurse Brown is an astute young woman, who knows what she wants and means to get it,' he replied ambiguously.

'What does that mean?' she asked, frowning, and he shrugged.

'How should I know? But be careful, Christy—you were in danger of ousting her before that convenient marriage.'

'Meaning?'

'Meaning that if she suspected the truth, she might make trouble.'

'She's no proof—anyway, if she wants to hook Gramp and he's willing, why should I care?'

'As long as Fairmile's safe, I imagine,' he suggested dryly, and before she could reply, Rose Brown came into the room. Her hair was neatly subdued again and her over-

86

all buttoned and concealing. She gave a soft little exclamation of disapproval as she surveyed the still uncleared table and rang the bell for Tom.

'Things have become rather disorganized today, I'm afraid,' she observed with the automatic apology of the experienced hostess. 'I shall have to speak to Tom; he's getting a little past it, poor dear. Did you see your grandfather, Christy?'

Christy had joined Joss by the window, trying not to look, as she felt, like a sulky child.

'Yes,' she replied. 'And he asked if you would sit with him. He was complaining again of a headache, but he's asleep, I think.'

'That will do him good. Yes, I will certainly sit with him. What will you two do with yourselves for the rest of the afternoon?' The nurse's intonation was so exactly that of the lady of the house that Christy's too-recent ill temper returned to assert itself.

Before she could speak, however, Joss suddenly swept her up into his arms and planted a kiss full on her lips.

'Oh, we shall amuse ourselves. A newly married couple aren't too hard put to it to pass the time, you know,' he said, and Brown, with slightly compressed lips, left the room without replying.

'What on earth made you do that?' Christy demanded furiously as, none too gently, he set her on her feet again.

'To allay the suspicions she obviously harbours that all is not well between us, also to stop you picking a quarrel with her,' he replied cheerfully. 'Pity you had to struggle so obviously.'

'You,' said Christy, 'are the most exasperating man I've ever met! Don't try any more of those capers for Brown's benefit or anyone else's!'

CHAPTER FIVE

BUT of course he did. He might have been quite logical in his excuses, but Christy suspected that he took a slightly malicious pleasure in disconcerting her with sudden demonstrations of affection. In time, however, she came rather to enjoy paying him back in his own coin. For her grandfather's benefit, and een for Brown's, she would trustingly lift up her face, demanding a kiss which he could not very well refuse, but the first time she, of her own accord, put her arms round him in a lingering embrace, she surprised a very curious expression on his face.

'Didn't you like it?' she asked innocently when they were alone, and he gave her a long and rather peculiar stare.

'You'd better watch your step,' was all he said, and she smiled happily.

'You're quite safe. I'm not your type—remember?' she replied sedately, and he grinned.

'Very brave when there's company around, aren't you?' he retorted. 'Our rooms have a communicating door with no key in the lock, don't forget.'

'You wouldn't dare! Why, I'd scream the place down!'

'Which might look rather odd, don't you think? A husband has a perfect right in his wife's bedroom.'

But she was not so bold as her words and actions implied, he observed with amusement when, that night, he heard her prop a chair under the handle of the door between their rooms. He wondered if she would remember to remove it in the morning before Brown brought up the early tea.

But as the days slipped imperceptibly by, Christy recognized a change in herself. Although Joss could still goad her to childish retaliation, she had come to depend on him. When he showed her a brief unexpected tenderness, as on

88

the occasion when she had fallen out of the swing, her hostility was stilled, and perhaps it was no longer hostility she felt for him, for, in some curious fashion, he had become part of Fairmile, which meant that in some small measure he must also have become part of herself.

'Have you ever been made love to?' he asked her once, as they sat in the sun on the old mounting block in the stable yard.

'Naturally,' she replied, looking surprised. 'I know quite a few young men.'

'Naturally,' he mimicked her gravely. 'But you've never been in love.'

She sighed. 'I've tried, but I usually end up with the giggles, which rather shocks them. My suitors are rather young and callow, I'm afraid. I prefer older men.'

'Do you indeed? And do you know any?'

'No. Only the bottom-pinching type—and you, of course.'

'Thanks very much!'

She grinned with mock apology, and the sunlight fell warmly on her skin, revealing the faint, rather touching suggestion of down belonging to the very young.

'Now it's my turn to be nosey,' she said. 'Have *you* ever been in love?'

'My dear child, I'm thirty-five—nearly thirty-six! I'm hardly without experience!'

'Oh, I don't mean tarts and the obliging wives of business acquaintances. All men go through that.'

She really was rather charmingly naïve.

'What a curious generalization of the male sex!' he observed. 'Have you lost your illusions at twenty?'

'I haven't illusions of that kind,' she said. 'On the Continent one learns to take that sort of thing in one's stride. It's not important. Aren't you going to tell me?'

'No. You talk a great deal of nonsense, Christobel.'

'Now you're annoyed with me. You said you'd address me

as Christobel when I annoyed you. I wasn't prying, you know—only curious. I think you'd make rather an exciting lover, as a matter of fact.'

'Do you, now? Would you like me to give you a demonstration?' He made a move towards her with rather a menacing air, and she withdrew in sudden alarm, then caught the twinkle in his eye and gave him that wide, endearing smile.

'What a clot I am!' she exclaimed, crinkling up her eyes at him.

'Good!' he said approvingly. 'You're learning to laugh at yourself.'

'You think I take myself too seriously?'

'Perhaps—or not seriously enough. You're a bit of an egotist, aren't you? But a sense of humour isn't an attribute of the very young. That comes with the years and the vulgar kick or two in the pants life's apt to deal you. Then it becomes a necessity.'

Her eyes held a shy, unfamiliar tenderness as they dwelt on his hard-bitten profile, remembering the orphanage and the tough, rough life of the backwoods.

'You've had a good few kicks, haven't you, Joss?' she said, and he grinned.

'Oh, I've had my share, but I don't doubt I asked for 'em!'

'I,' she told him, after due consideration, 'quite frequently want to kick you myself, so perhaps you do ask for it.'

He laughed. 'I know you do! Well, dear Christobel, if you ever do, I shall administer that spanking we've spoken of, so there will be satisfaction on both sides. You have been warned!'

'You,' she said, suddenly on her dignity, 'quite often tell me to grow up, but you persist in treating me as a child. Not very consistent, is it?'

'*Touché* . . .' he murmured, turning down his mouth. 'I

must mend my ways. You're so refreshing to tease, Christy, it's apt to become a habit.'

'Then it's a habit you should get out of,' she retorted severely.

'Why? Do you mind?'

'No,' she said, sounding surprised, 'I don't believe I do.'

And in some measure that became true. It was familiar and right to see him pushing her grandfather's chair about the grounds, to listen to his suggestions for renovating the place, to hear old Tom refer to him as one of the family. Only the nurse seemed to stand apart, quiet and watchful, with that little secret smile on her lips. But every so often Christy would surprise a hungry look in her eyes as they dwelt on Joss, even while her tongue was replying with colourless decorum to his casual remarks.

She wanted Joss, Christy discovered with surprised interest. Brown, she knew now, would become Lady Tavener, given the opportunity, but she wanted Joss as well. The realization which, at first, had brought only curiosity and faint amusement now began to inspire other emotions. She did not care for the experienced regard with which he sometimes studied the nurse and, without understanding why, she frequently found it difficult to be civil to either of them.

'What's biting you, monkey?' Sir Harry would ask, and then roar with laughter. 'Jealous, are you?'

'Jealous! If Joss fancies Brown why should I care?' she exclaimed unguardedly, and the old man's beard bristled with sudden impatience.

'Queer remark to make about your bridegroom, I must say!' he snorted. 'Don't understand this modern generation. In my young day we kept our wives and mistresses decently apart. None of this share and share alike business to prove how civilized we were.'

'I'm not *that* civilized. I'm not sharing any man with

another woman,' Christy retorted, and he grinned approvingly.

'That's my girl. Jealous, as I said, and quite natural, too, but don't waste your spleen on poor Brown. She's a good, competent woman who knows her place.'

'That's all *you* know,' Christy snapped. 'For two pins she'd marry you and have an affair right under your nose with my husband.'

'Good God, girl! Are you off your rocker?' he exploded. 'Don't say much for your opinion of either of 'em, if that's the way you think.'

Christy looked a little abashed. She had, she supposed, been talking at random; it was so easy to whip up half-truths into monstrous facts.

'I don't suppose I really do,' she said, grinning a little ruefully. 'Joss calls me a spoilt brat. Would you agree?'

'He's not far out at that, but *I* didn't do the spoiling—never had the chance.'

'You never wanted the chance—you cut us all out!'

But for once he had not rise to the familiar challenge, and his face merely expressed the irritability which seemed to be growing on him.

'That old bone of contention's grown whiskers,' he said. 'Go and pick a quarrel with your husband if you want a fight. He'll be a match for you.'

She smiled at him affectionately, the desire to pick a quarrel with anyone already dead.

'You like him, don't you, Gramp?' she said, and he grinned.

'He'll do. Run away, Christy, you're too adolescent for me at times. It exhausts me. Go and find Brown.'

'Would you marry her, Gramp, or were you just boasting?' she asked a little wistfully.

'Well, now, mightn't it be the sensible thing to do?' he replied with a rather wicked twinkle. 'No guarantee she'd stay for ever once you've gone. She's told me so. Tie her down, wouldn't it?'

'Yes, I supppose so, only—I wouldn't like to think she could snatch Fairmile from me so easily,' she said, and his bushy eyebrows rose.

'And what use will Fairmile be to you, may I ask, if you're to make your home in Canada?' he retorted slyly.

She went away to look for Joss, hopeful that he might suggest some way out of the impasse, but as she wandered through the house, peering into empty rooms, it was as if Fairmile itself had also suffered a sea-change. Why had she never realized how shabby it had become, how many rooms were closed, and the furniture shrouded in dust sheets? For the first time she noticed damp patches and crumbling cornices; the stuffed peacocks had the moth and should have been discarded long ago, and curtains and rugs were faded and frayed. Fairmile, for her, could never quite lose its magic, but she suddenly saw it as Joss clearly had, a place out-dated which had been allowed to drop into gentle decay, and she wondered whether Gramp, confined to his wheelchair, had not noticed sufficiently to put things to rights, or if he no longer cared.

Upstairs, she wandered from her own room into Joss's, idly examining his scattered belongings. His few possessions were good, if not new, she discovered curiously; suits built by a fairly exclusive tailor, shoes hand-made and the ivory-backed brushes bore the entwined initials, R.L.C. So Tavener, as she had suspected all along, was not his real name. His duplicity in taking advantage of her grandfather's credulity seemed, in that illogical moment, to be on a par with her own for passing him off for what he was not.

She stared broodingly at the bed. It was the twin of her own, with identical posts and drapes. It seemed odd to think of him occupying such a blatantly marital couch, and she wondered idly if he sprawled across it, taking up the whole with masculine ease, or slept decorously to one side, as she did in hers.

She found him eventually at work on the topiary, and stood and watched with surprise the rough skill with which he was trimming the yews to their original shapes.

'Where did you learn this kind of work?' she asked curiously. 'I thought it was rather specialized.'

'Oh, one picks up various trades as a rolling stone,' he replied. She did not retort, as usual, but sat down on the grass, spreading her skirt carefully around her.

'It's very neglected, isn't it? I hadn't noticed before,' she said, and he gave her a quick glance over his shoulder.

'A topiary soon gets out of hand,' he replied. 'Not enough gardeners for the size of the place.'

'I didn't mean just the topiary—I mean all of it. I've just been prowling round the house. It's funny, but I've never noticed until now.'

'You never knew it, I understand, in more spacious times when labour was cheap and plentiful.'

'Only when I was very little, and a child doesn't notice such things. My mother made the magic for me out of *her* memories, I suppose, and I had nothing to compare.'

'And now you're disappointed—even feel a bit cheated?'

'No, of course not. Nothing can really alter Fairmile, but I can't understand why Gramp, with all his money, hasn't taken more care of it.'

Joss clipped away in silence for a while, and she watched the strong muscles of his back which were discernible through the thin material of his shirt.

'Your grandfather has been living on capital for some years,' he said, after a pause. 'He's probably not as well off as you imagine.'

'How do you know? Does he discuss his affairs with you?'

'Oh yes, but that's quite natural, don't you think?'

'No, I don't. I'm his granddaughter and you, after all, are only a stranger.'

'Well, he comes of a generation which kept matters of

94

business from the ears of the ladies. And who but his supposed grandson-in-law is more suitable as a confidant, now?'

'Your brushes have different initials from yours,' she said abruptly. 'What's your real name?'

'Been having a gentle snoop?' he inquired with irritating composure. 'Never be misled by deceptive appearances, Christobel. Did you think I'd pinched them?'

She did not trouble to answer, but sat staring out across the parkland.

The little property, still isolated from the spreading ugliness of housing development and the creeping tentacles of factory-ridden new towns, had seemed traditionally beautiful to her unaccustomed eyes, but now she could see the neglect in fences and boundaries, the sad spirit of capitulation to the harsher demands of an age which had no room for the impoverished landowner. Impoverished? But Gramp was rich! Ill-health and disappointment at the absence of a male heir must have made him indifferent or, perhaps, simply unobservant.

Joss was so surprised at not receiving the expected retort that he stopped his work and turned to look at her.

'What is it?' he asked, with a change of voice, and flinging down his shears, he knelt in the grass beside her.

'Oh Joss . . .' she said, sounding suddenly tremulous, and he put a hand under her chin, turning her face up to his.

'What's upset you? Been having words with Nurse Brown?'

'Brown? No. It's just that everything's going wrong. I— I've got myself into a mess by this silly game, and now Gramp says what use will Fairmile be to me anyway if I'm to make my home in Canada?'

'What use, indeed?' he remarked calmly, and saw a flash of the old hostility come into the eyes that had seemed at one time to be filling with tears.

'Why do you encourage him to think I'm going with you

to Canada?' she demanded. 'You could at least pretend you mean to settle here. He likes you, and he wants great-grandsons.'

'What an improper suggestion, considering we're not married,' he retorted. 'As a matter of fact I've hardly mentioned Canada. It's helpful Nurse Brown who has our future all nicely mapped out for us.'

'Brownie? Well, naturally she's angling to get rid of me so that she can bring Gramp up to scratch, and I can't blame her for wanting to secure her own future, only——'

'Only what?'

'I won't have her making sheep's eyes at my husband as well.'

He sat back on his heels and gave her a long look, one eyebrow rising a little higher than the other.

'Very flattering of you, my dear, but may I remind you that you haven't got a husband—yet?' he drawled, and saw the colour mount under her skin.

'What do you mean by yet?' she asked, still with that uncharacteristic reasonableness.

'Never mind for now. You know, Christy, you're very feminine in your lack of logic. You've convinced yourself that Fairmile is yours by right, and you've almost convinced yourself that we really are married.'

'I've done nothing of the sort!' she protested, rising to the bait at last. 'Do you think I could tolerate you for a moment—your overbearing ways, your conceit, your—your pretence of being what you're not!'

'All those things?' he said gently, and pulled her suddenly into his arms.

'Why not stop fighting me?' he asked softly, and kissed her, feeling her lips move involuntarily under his, even though she tried to pull away.

'There's no need for that now. No one's about to see us,' she protested, but he only held her more firmly.

'And that's a very good reason, don't you think?' he said,

and kissed her again.

Her anger melted away and she felt herself become pliant and receptive, things that no man had made her feel before. She found she knew instinctively the way to yield, the way to trace with shy desire the bones of his face with tender fingers.

'Well now . . .' he said, releasing her, '. . . you do surprise me, Christobel. Who taught you to make love so charmingly?'

'No one taught me——' she began with honesty, then added hastily: 'At least, unless you count——'

'Spare me the imaginary list of suitors,' he interrupted. 'You don't need to play-act with me, my dear. You're quite inexperienced, aren't you?'

'What are you trying to do, Joss?' she said, rubbing the back of her hand across her mouth. 'Aren't you content with making a hit with Gramp and Tom and Mrs. Heap—even Brown? Must you add my scalp, too, to all the others?'

His smile was tender as he got to his feet, pulling her after him and remarking that the grass was damp.

'You talk a great deal of nonsense,' he said. 'Now run away and let me get on with my job.'

'You—you haven't,' she began, feeling suddenly shy of him, 'suggested any way out of the mess.'

'The mess was of your making. You must find your own way out,' he retorted, picking up the shears. 'And by the way, doesn't it occur to you that we're overstaying our welcome? It's the first of October tomorrow and I was hired, as you put it, for a week or two at the most.'

'I couldn't foresee—well, lots of things. Gramp's attack and—and his taking to you as he has.'

'True, but I have a living to think of. Putting things on a more sordid basis, I've done nearly a fortnight's overtime.'

His back was towards her and he had begun clipping again. Christy was not sure at that moment whether she wanted to hit him or burst into tears.

'If it's more money you want, then I'm prepared to pay,' she said, her nose in the air.

'Can you afford it?' he asked, and she replied, stiffly:

'I'll see that I can.'

He turned then, just for a moment, to give her an odd look over his shoulder.

'We'll settle for the other two-fifty. I'll take payment for overtime in another fashion,' he said, and she turned and walked away without another word.

All the way back to the house she could hear the sound of the shears and his careless whistling, and the tears filled her eyes at last and spilled over.

Nothing seemed quite so carefree after that day. Christy, to restore confidence in herself, was rude to Joss, given the opportunity, but, uncharacteristically, she began to worry: about Fairmile's ultimate fate, about her grandfather's health, about Brown's place in their lives, and the unknown quantity which was Joss, and above all, a way out of her own light-hearted deception least calculated to hurt Sir Harry.

She waylaid the doctor on one of his visits, demanding a straight answer as to the seriousness of the heart attacks, but only received an encouraging pat on the head. The doctor was old-fashioned and accustomed to giving evasive replies to awkward questions, and, if pressed, became vague and avuncular. He referred her to Brown whom he admired discreetly, stating firmly that Sir Harry could not be in better hands.

'Fine woman, that,' he said, puffing out his pink cheeks. 'Selfless devotion, my dear, selfless devotion. Never a day off ... only hope she gets her reward.'

'Silly old fool!' thought Christy, wondering what insinuations of self-sacrifice Brown had let fall during the past few months. Of course she had time off, but what she did with it and where she went, no one had troubled to inquire.

'Why don't you join us in the dining-room as usual if you're not going out?' Christy asked her once, and the nurse gave a little smile.

'One's employers need a break just as one does oneself,' she replied. 'I wouldn't like Sir Harry to feel he was stuck with me just because I prefer to remain here when I'm off duty.'

Very praiseworthy, thought Christy, unimpressed, even to carrying her trays up and down stairs and probably washing the dishes to save the servants extra work. But lately she had taken to looking in on them before going to bed, stopping to drink a nightcap with her patient, aware, no doubt, that out of her uniform overalls, with her hair loose and the slightly disturbing alteration of make-up, the men, at least, were made aware of her as a woman.

About this time Joss went to London once or twice for the day on some unspecified business, taking Christy's car, and on one occasion he offered Brown a lift since it was her day off.

Christy watched them drive away with mixed feelings. There was no reason why they should not travel together, to go their separate ways in town and meet again for the return journey, but the nurse's expression was smug and faintly proprietorial as she settled herself beside Joss in the car, her hat much too smart, and the look she gave Christy as she waved good-bye held a little gleam of triumph.

'Brown is really very good-looking when she's all dolled up,' Christy, trying to be generous, observed to her grandfather, and he grinned.

'Always told you so,' he retorted. 'You don't like them going off together, do you my girl?'

'Why on earth should *I* care? Poor Brown doesn't have much fun, stuck down here.'

'So you won't grudge her a little attention from your husband?'

'If you can call a lift to London and back attention, why should I?'

'You sound too tolerant, m'dear. What's the betting he stands her a nice little luncheon somewhere quiet and discreet and not too expensive?'

Christy shook her hair back impatiently. He was, she knew from past experience, only trying to get a rise out of her, but her temper began to simmer for all that.

'I couldn't care less if he does,' she snapped. 'What Joss chooses to do with his time is none of my business. He's a free agent.'

Sir Harry gave an irritable sigh.

'You young marrieds!' he exclaimed. 'No wonder the papers are full of divorces. Your husband *should* be your business unless you want to head for a crack-up.'

She began to push his chair along the terrace, searching in her mind for words. Despite her annoyance that Joss had chosen to offer Brown a lift without once having suggested that Christy herself might like a day in London, she had welcomed the opportunity to be alone with her grandfather and find by gentle probing a way out of the tangle.

'Our—our marriage was very much a thing of impulse,' she began, glad that she was walking behind him and he could not see the rather wretched embarrassment in her face. 'You may say you don't understand my generation, Gramp, but surely it's better to part company if a marriage doesn't work out and—and try again?'

'What in hell do you mean?' he suddenly roared. 'You're not trying to tell me, I hope, that after a couple of months you're already sick of the feller!'

'No—no, of course not, only—well, if we found we weren't right for each other, you wouldn't expect us to stick it out to the grave just for the look of things, would you?'

'Yes, I would. Stop pushing this damned chair and come round here where I can see you.'

She turned the chair to face his favourite view across the

parkland, and perched herself with a little sigh on the stone balustrade which bordered the terrace.

'Now then, young woman,' he said, fixing his fierce old eyes on her unhappy face. 'What bee in your bonnet have you got in your head this time? Talking of parting company just because Joss has taken the nurse for a joy-ride instead of you!'

'Of course not,' she said impatiently. 'I'm afraid you don't understand, Gramp, and what I'm going to tell you will come as a bit of a shock. I—I didn't really mean to deceive, but I was angry and—well you see, Joss and I aren't really——'

'If you're going to tell me again you aren't suited, I won't listen!' he shouted, and brought both hands down on the arms of his chair in the familiar gesture of anger and exasperation.

'Now listen to me, Christy. You married on impulse—or said you did—to pay me out. Very well, I accept that, but what I won't accept is any attempt to wriggle out of a commitment the easy way. The Taveners have their faults, but not sticking by their bargains isn't one of them. There's been no divorce in our family as far back as I can remember, and further, and I won't have it, do you understand?'

She looked at him helplessly. This was not Gramp in one of his familiar hectoring moods, but an old, tired man whose convictions could not be overruled by wheedling.

'You wouldn't be able to stop it,' she said a little wearily.

'No, not in law, but if you want Fairmile, you'll stay married.'

'What do you mean?'

'You know very well. I'm not, mind you, making any promises, but if I *do* alter my existing will, it will have conditions, and I think I've made it plain what they would be.'

'Oh, Gramp . . .' she said, and suddenly began to cry. How could she explain now that the whole situation was false? He looked a little blue about the lips and she remembered Brown's quiet hints that a shock could do fatal damage. It had all seemed so easy in theory to disappear abroad and pretend to a divorce, but she had not understood until now how strongly he felt about such things or, indeed, how much she had probably shocked him.

'If only I could tell you without hurting you,' she said, longing for confession, and he looked at the fair drooping head, so like her mother's, and his anger and disappointment began to seep away.

'Now, don't cry,' he growled, irritated because, even now, a woman's tears could upset him. 'You're jealous, m'dear, and that's all it boils down to—very natural, too, and shows you aren't as indifferent to that man of yours as you'd like to make out. You're young, Christy, and I think you've picked a chap too old and experienced to have much time for adolescent vapours, but don't go throwing tantrums because he can look with an appreciative eye on another woman. Do you want a stuffed dummy for a husband?'

She looked up then and gave him the tremulous beginnings of the wide smile he loved. How could she argue with him now, how deliver one shock greater than the other?

'It isn't jealousy,' she said. 'At least, I don't think so. I—I don't really know what Joss's taste in women might be, but he's certainly no stuffed dummy.'

'He married you, didn't he? You're not, I hope, so simple as to think a man of his age would be without experience of women? Grow up, my girl, and get down to the fundamentals of life. Don't let the bit of money that's given you independence make you think you know all the answers. You have a lot to learn yet, Christy.'

'Yes . . .' she said, 'yes . . .' and because it was no longer possible to make confession, she asked humbly for forgiveness for being foolish.

'That's better,' Sir Harry said, relaxing more comfortably in his chair. 'We'll make a small occasion of it when they come back this evening, shall we? Champagne, and you in your prettiest frock.'

'Why?' she demanded suspiciously.

'No particular reason, unless you feel like wiping Brown's eye,' he replied innocently, and as he watched the soft hesitation creep into her young face, he gave his familiar wicked chuckle. 'Wear the white thing you had on that night you told me you were married. You haven't treated us to much more than those hideous pants you seem to like so much. Were you married in that?'

'In what?' she asked vaguely, trying to sort out the various implications in his remarks.

'That white garment that makes you look like your mother.'

'No,' she answered truthfully enough, and he said, sounding suddenly tired:

'Wheel me back to the house, will you? I'll rest for a bit in my room. Tom will help me.'

She turned the chair and pushed it slowly back along the terrace, sharply aware of the autumn sadness which had fallen upon the land. The drifts of leaves, the branches of trees showing their first skeleton bareness, the withering grass, and the old man in his chair, his white head sunk on his chest, spoke in mute tones of decay and finality, and Christy shivered. How could things change so much because of one moment of folly? she wondered. Why should she become suddenly aware of so much that had been taken for granted before?

She looked down at the network of lines and wrinkles which puckered her grandfather's neck, and felt the tears spring to her eyes again. He must be seventy ... eighty ... she did not know; but she thought with sharp regret of the years of her mother's exile, when he, a stubborn, lonely old man, had lived in unyielding solitude in a corner of this great house which was falling slowly into decay about him.

'Those peacocks have the moth,' she observed aloud, and smiled tenderly as she saw his head jerk back. 'You were asleep, Gramp.'

'Asleep? Nonsense! I'm not in my dotage,' he grunted. 'What peacocks?'

'The stuffed ones at the foot of the stairs. Why do you keep them?'

'Your mother liked them—when they were alive, that is. She used to feed them when she was a little girl.'

They had reached the house and Tom came out to help with the chair.

'And well I remember, Sir Harry, sir,' he said with a special smile for Christy, whom, as a small child, he had obligingly pushed in the swing for hours, just as he had probably done at an earlier date for her mother. 'Used to screech and peck at her legs, poor mite—funny, isn't it, when you look back all those years?'

'Stuff and nonsense!' barked Sir Harry. 'Never look back—doesn't do. Get me on to my bed, Tom. I'm tired— and I want champagne brought up tonight, and the Georgian glasses.'

'Is it a celebration, sir?' the old servant asked, looking surprised.

'Perhaps—eh, Christy? And don't forget that white dress.'

Christy's composure returned as she saw her grandfather's familiar twinkle. Whatever he might be up to, he was, she observed, his old self again and she stooped to kiss him.

'Very well, Gramp,' she said, anxious to gratify whatever whim he might have because she had so nearly shattered his peace of mind. But as she went upstairs to inspect the white crêpe which had not been worn since the summer, she thought with wry affection that the average male fancy for a garment had little to do with the suitability of the season.

She heard the car return while she was still dressing, but she did not hurry. She owed it to Gramp at least to make an entrance, and indeed she was finding herself possessed of a certain excitement, pinning the hair high on her crown to effect a change, being meticulous and cunning with cosmetics and scent, inspecting critically any small blemish that might mar the carefully contrived whole. For what? For Gramp, who had issued the idle challenge? For Brown, whose eye she might care to wipe? For Joss, who could offer a rare and unlikely compliment but who seldom thought of her as adult?

On this last reflection, she revolved slowly before the long old-fashioned pier-glass, trying to see herself with his eyes. Would he find her charming, possibly a little exciting, or would his lazy regard tell her that she was still only play-acting and not to be taken seriously?

'I'll make him!' she said aloud to her reflection, then held her breath as she heard him enter the room next door. His movements were familiar to her now, the sound of his shoes being kicked off, the creak of the cupboard door when he hung up his coat, the small muffled noises of objects picked up and replaced on the dressing-table. There was still no key in the lock of their communicating door, but he seldom opened it, even to call out good night, and it was somewhat disappointing that the only occasion when she had propped a chair under the door handle had drawn no comment from him.

She frowned, wondering what had taken him to London, wondering, too, whether he had really given Brown lunch, wondering what his background really was and how much of her two hundred and fifty pounds he had left. She should, she supposed a little uncomfortably, write him a cheque for the rest, since, as he had pointed out, he had already far exceeded the terms of their contract. But she was beginning to experience a reluctance to discuss money with him, which, of course, was absurd since he had made it quite plain that he lived by his wits.

She heard him leave his room, gave him a few more minutes to get settled with her grandfather, then went downstairs to join them.

After that first evening they had never used the musty library for their aperitifs, but had reverted to the familiar focus-point of Sir Harry's study, which was shabby and invariably littered with ancient newspapers and journals and the strange assortment of junk which had accumulated through the years. It was, thought Christy, pausing for a moment in the doorway, the heart of the house. Here you could forget about the scores of shrouded rooms, the emptiness and dust and the waste of gracious beauty. For perhaps the first time she recognized the truth of her grandfather's words when he had told her, back in the summer, that she could never afford to keep up Fairmile on the income she had at present. *I don't want your money*, she had retorted many times, so ignorant, in her new-found independence, of the cost which a big estate must entail; but Brown must have known when she had hinted so idly that a compromise could be effected between the place and the money. But if it was true that Brown meant to marry Gramp, then she meant to have Fairmile too.

'What on earth are you staring at? You look as if you've seen a ghost! Come in and let's have a look at you,' Sir Harry barked irritably, and Christy, whose spectre had, for the moment, seemed quite real, became aware of them all, Joss rising politely, his lips touched with a fleeting smile of amusement, Rose Brown lying back in a chair, elegant and a little disturbing in her smart London clothes. Illogically she had not expected Brown to join them since she was off duty, then, her eyes going from her grandfather's suddenly mischievous expression to the iced bucket of champagne on the trolley, her heart gave an unpleasant little jerk. A small celebration, he had said, and she had taken it arrogantly as a compliment to herself; but was it not possible that he had a surprise of his own to spring and, for all she knew, Joss as well as Brown might be in the secret?

She walked lightly across the room to kiss her grandfather, smiled serenely at the nurse, and gave Joss a quick challenging look from under her lashes which made him smile again.

'Well...' he observed with a faint accentuation of Canadian accent, 'here's a thing, and a very pretty thing ... How long did that hair-style take you, my poppet?'

'I just bundled it up, and I am not a poppet,' she replied somewhat coldly, and his smile became a grin.

'Does me credit, eh, Joss—eh, Brown?' chuckled Sir Harry. Joss made no reply, but the nurse said with a soft little inflection of amusement:

'Very charming—very bridal,' and Christy coloured faintly. Were they trying to put ideas into Joss's head? she wondered, then remembered that as far as they were concerned she was presumed to be already married to him, but as she felt Joss's arm go round her drawing her firmly down on to the arm of his chair, she suspected the same notion had occurred to him, and she wriggled uneasily.

'Not comfortable?' he inquired with innocent concern. 'Perhaps my knee might be better.'

'I'm perfectly comfortable, thanks,' she said, well aware that he was quite capable of pulling her on to his knee whether she liked it or not.

'Well, you can leave the billing and cooing till later and open the champagne,' grinned Sir Harry, and, as Joss rose to comply, Christy slipped neatly into his vacated chair and sat there with feet together and demurely folded hands.

'Well now,' Sir Harry said, when their glasses were charged, 'what shall the toast be tonight? To your happiness, of course, Christy—and to your husband's, but I think we have drunk that already. Brown, have I ever expressed my appreciation of your services—and devotion? We'll drink to Brown, I think.'

This was it, Christy thought, as she raised her glass and watched, with interest, the expressions which chased themselves across the nurse's face; surprise, expectancy and at last complacency. She was, thought Christy with impartial honesty, a very personable young woman in her quiet fashion, and it was surprising that she should have been taken for granted. She smiled upon them with easy graciousness and raised her own glass to Sir Harry in a return salute.

'To my favourite patient,' she said, and he grinned.

'And to our future partnership, I hope,' he replied. 'When Christy leaves us we will become Darby and Joan again, what?'

Brown's eyebrows lifted inquiringly as she sipped her champagne, but she said nothing, and the old man added, with his sly delight in angling for a rise:

'Not that I can hope to keep such a charming lady in chains for ever. It's a sad thing to be old and crippled and unwanted.'

Christy gave a brief grin at such blatant hypocrisy, but the nurse, lowering her lashes for a moment in the familiar look of secrecy, replied with composure.

'You do yourself an injustice, Sir Harry, as I think you very well know. And women are not averse to chains, as you call them, if they bring their own rewards.'

Well, that was a plain enough hint, anyway, Christy thought, almost expecting her grandfather to propose then and there, but Sir Harry, whatever his ultimate intention, liked, she knew, to keep everyone guessing.

'Well, now!' he exclaimed, opening his bright blue eyes very wide. 'What can you mean by that, Brown?'

'I think you know very well, Sir Harry,' the nurse replied demurely, and Christy, not liking this cat-and-mouse game at all, spilt a little champagne on her dress.

'Oh, what a shame!' Brown exclaimed softly. 'Such a pretty dress, and so suitable for a young bride.'

Was there mockery in her calm voice? Christy wondered, flinging up her head to retaliate, but Joss was already bending over her, dabbing at the stain with a clean pocket handkerchief.

'Easy now,' he murmured. 'Don't let them stampede you.'

His eyes held kindness as well as amusement, and she felt absurdly grateful to him, though for what, she had little idea.

'It is, isn't it?' she said sweetly. 'Joss chose it.'

'I thought you told me you weren't married in it?' Sir Harry said sharply.

'I wasn't,' she replied with more calmness that she felt. 'But that's no reason why Joss shouldn't choose it, is it?'

'None at all,' said Brown soothingly. 'Only you had that dress when you were here in the summer—remember?'

'We were married quite early in the summer, Nurse Brown,' Joss observed, returning the handkerchief to his breast pocket with care, and Sir Harry gave a sudden and unexpected bellow of laughter.

'Good for you, me boy!' he exclaimed with rather inexplicable enjoyment, and Brown moved a little restlessly in her chair.

'Of course,' she said, then added with innocent inquiry: 'Did you think we were doubting you, Mr. Tavener?'

'I think,' Christy interposed with an edge to her voice, 'that we've all had enough double talk. May I have some more champagne, please?'

When Joss had refilled the glasses he did not return to his position beside Christy's chair, but propped himself against Sir Harry's littered desk to observe her with greater ease. She had a fresh piquancy with her flaxen hair piled high; the surprising contrast of dark eyebrows seemed more marked with the sharp, clear outlines of her cheekbones exposed, and he saw, as he observed her summer tan was rapidly fading, that her skin would be as white as the dress she wore. He became conscious that the old man's eyes were upon him with quizzical amusement and removed his own regard from Christy.

'Well?' barked Sir Harry with teasing malice. 'Have a good day in town? Bet you didn't waste too much time on business—eh, Brown?'

'I wouldn't know, Sir Harry,' Brown replied, with a little smile.

'Wouldn't you! Well, Christy and I had our own ideas, didn't we, monkey?' He winked unblushingly at his grand-daughter, who managed to smile upon him with charming tolerance. Joss said:

'Business, as it happened, occupied most of my day. By the way, Christy, I bought you a present.'

'O-*ho*!' Sir Harry chuckled, delighted. 'It's always suspicious when the husband comes bearing gifts!'

'Gramp, you're impossible!' Christy retorted, and Joss was surprised to see that her cheeks had suddenly flushed like a child's. 'What is it, Joss? Let me see! You've never brought me a present before ...' She tailed off uncertainly, aware of Joss's sudden frown and the raised eyebrows of the other two.

'I mean——' she began inconclusively, but Joss had turned away.

'Later,' he said. 'I hope it's what you like. Rose chose it.'

'*Rose?*'

If he was disconcerted, Christy saw no signs of it.

'Nurse Brown prefers to be called by her Christian name when she's off duty. She says it makes her feel more human,' he replied, and Sir Harry cocked a speculative eye at the nurse.

'Rose—that's a pretty name. It suits you,' he said, and Brown took a meditative sip from her glass.

'I don't care much for flower names, myself,' she observed with composure. 'But I confess it's pleasant to be remembered sometimes as a person and not a uniform.'

Christy remembered with humility the many times when she had taken Brown for granted, accepting small services, giving carelessly of her gratitude in the form of small presents. The hostility which she had recently felt for the nurse vanished in self-reproach and she said generously:

'Would you like us to call you Rose? Would it make you feel better?'

'If it pleases you,' Brown replied indifferently. 'But I doubt if you could break the habit now.'

Christy felt chilled and looked down into her empty glass without speaking, but Sir Harry murmured with a rather tired nostalgia:

'In my youth flower names were all the rage. Rose ... Lily ... Violet ... Pansy ...'

'Not Pansy, Gramp—that would be too much!' exclaimed Christy on a faintly hysterical note, and held out her glass to Joss, but he put it down on the trolley without refilling it.

'Please,' she said with sudden coolness, but he smiled and shook his head.

'Two's enough,' he said. 'Remember that night at St. Bede when I had to put you to bed?'

'*Well!*' He was, she supposed, at his old game of trying to corner her in front of the others, but it wasn't fair, she thought, that he could alternate so quickly between that and a mood of apparent tenderness.

'That's the stuff—begin as you mean to go on,' Sir Harry applauded, but it was only perfunctory teasing and the vigour had gone out of his voice.

Rose Brown, after a quick look at him, became immediately professional and familiar.

'You've been overdoing it, Sir Harry,' she chided, automatically feeling for his pulse. 'You're tired, aren't you?'

'A little, my dear, a little—and that headache's back again.'

111

'Would you like me to get you to bed and have a tray sent to your room?'

'No, no—you're off duty, anyway.'

But she had already begun to turn his chair round to face the door and now she bent over him, her face softened to gentleness and a brief, personal concern.

'I'm never off duty where a patient is concerned,' she told him reprovingly. 'And you, dear Sir Harry, are rather more than a patient. Come along—I'm going to tuck you up.'

'Two-faced bitch!' Christy remarked conversationally, as the door closed behind them, and reached for a cigarette. Joss raised his eyebrows.

'Really, Christobel, such langauge!' he observed, but poured out half a glass of champagne as compensation for his own teasing.

'Thank you,' she said, snatching it from him, and getting smoke in her eyes at the same time. 'And you needn't look so smug, Josiah Tavener—you haven't contributed much to the evening's gaiety.'

'Aren't you being a little harsh, darling? After all, I *have* brought you a present.'

'You needn't bring that up—I don't want to see it! Chosen by Rose, indeed! And don't call me darling when we're alone.'

'Can it be that you're jealous, dar—— I beg your pardon, Christobel?'

It was too much ... first Gramp, and now the insufferable Joss himself! Tears of goaded endurance, and of inexplicable disappointment as well, began to run down her cheeks and she choked over her champagne and threw the half-finished cigarette into the grate.

Suddenly he was kneeling beside her as he had on that day she had fallen from the swing, and she read the same concern in his face.

'Christy ...' he said with gentleness, 'don't take my teas-

112

ing so seriously. Haven't I told you to learn to laugh at yourself? I was beginning to think you'd made a start.'

'Oh, Joss . . .' she wept, and spilt the rest of the champagne on her dress again as she bowed her head on his shoulder, turning at last to him for comfort.

CHAPTER SIX

THE days passed quietly enough after that evening. Sir Harry seemed tired and unconcerned with any of them; Brown reverted to her accustomed role of nurse-companion in the background, and Joss, for the moment, dropped his inclination to tease. Christy, who, in desultory moments, had taken up her painting again, even persuaded him to sit for her.

'I've never tried my hand at portraits,' she said. 'You ought to make a good study, don't you think?'

'A most unpromising subject, I should have thought,' he retorted, but he submitted with a good grace, more because he enjoyed their amicable sparring than that he imagined he could assist in the furtherance of a talent she clearly did not possess.

They would repair to the dusty library because she said the light was good, and he patiently held the many poses she dictated for the pleasure of watching her bent with solemn concentration over her work. She liked, he observed with amusement, to affect a Chelsea air on these occasions, tight black jeans and sandals, elaborately careless kerchiefs and hair scraped back into a pony-tail. She informed him seriously that she attended art school regularly when she was living at the flat in London.

'And do you walk about dressed like that?' he asked with interest.

'Of course, everyone does—the art students, I mean.'

'And that's half the fun, isn't it? You're not a hippie by any chance, Christy?'

'No, they're scruffy. What do you mean—it's half the fun?'

114

'Play-acting, dressing up. Do you take your classes seriously?'

'Of course,' she said again. 'One must do something.'

'You could work.'

'Why? I don't need money.'

'Of course, I was forgetting—the little rich girl with dollars to burn,' he said gravely. 'And where does art school get you?'

'Nowhere much, I suppose,' she answered cheerfully. 'My masters say I haven't any talent, but I learn a lot from watching other people, and I adore messing with paints— they're so gloriously gooey.'

'H'm ... you could get the same satisfaction from stirring up mud in the potholes in the avenue, I imagine.'

'You have no soul, Joss,' she told him with mild rebuke. 'There wouldn't be any colour.'

He laughed and got up to walk round behind her, ignoring her plea for five minutes longer.

'Can I look?' he asked, but his eyes dwelt absently on her, rather than on the portrait. Today she had abandoned her pony-tail and had pinned her hair on top of her head as she had worn it that evening of Sir Harry's not very successful little celebration, and he noticed with interest the tender look of the hollow in the nape of her neck.

'What an innocent neck you have,' he remarked, and she exclaimed impatiently:

'You aren't even *looking*! It's not very like you, I'm afraid, is it?'

He transferred his attention to the portrait with reluctance.

'H'm ...' he observed. 'I hope not! My nose surely can't be as long as that ...'

'Not quite, perhaps, but it *is* your nose—kind of bossy.'

'Bossy?'

'Yes, bossy. Let's go out.'

She enjoyed very much taking him to her favourite

places; Wet Wood where the pines stood like tall sentinels and made a sweet-smelling carpet of needles; Fishpond Shaw, already damp and marshy with the approach of autumn, and the mossy wastes of Coalpit, marred now by the first excavations of the new housing estate which would soon obliterate it.

'It's changed even since I first came here,' Christy said, gazing with angry dismay at the mushroom growth of bungalows and small, ugly houses which seemed to be springing up everywhere. 'Why does progress have to be so hideous?'

'You're a reactionary, Christy,' Joss told her with gentle irony. 'Rather surprising really, when you've lived abroad so much and haven't been brought up here.'

'Perhaps that's why,' she said. 'I've always imagined this place as it used to be when my mother was young. She told me so many stories and I never thought it could change—I suppose children don't. Fairmile is almost the last citadel in these parts, isn't it? Gramp, of course, hasn't an idea how things have encroached. He hasn't been outside the grounds for years.'

'Your grandpapa hardly shares your sentimental nostalgia, for all that,' he retorted. 'He told me that before he got to know you he was often tempted to sell the place. He would have got a good price as building land.'

'Building land—Fairmile!' she exclaimed, horrified. 'Rows of council houses in the park and the house turned into poky flats ... but, Joss, he never would—say he never would!'

'I don't suppose it's likely now, though he probably ought to. I wonder why you have such a fixation on the place.'

'Don't *you* think it's something special?'

'Not, I imagine, in the way you do. It's after all, a very minor relation of one of the Stately Homes, and has been allowed to sink into bad repair. Do you really imagine you'll be able to afford to live here, supposing the old man leaves it to you?'

'I don't know. I suppose not, on the money I've got, but it could become a hotel, or something, to pay for its upkeep, couldn't it?'

'And would you like that?'

'Not much, but at least it would be spared housing development, and it would be better than losing it. Did you know that Gramp is sending for his lawyer? That looks like a new will, doesn't it?'

'Yes, so I understand. I hope you won't be disappointed by the outcome.'

She regarded him with sudden misgiving.

'Do you mean you know what he has in mind?' she asked resentfully. 'It's hardly fair, do you think, to be all man-to-man with the old poppet when you're deceiving him up to the eyebrows?'

His regard was a mixture of amusement and gravity.

'I haven't deceived your grandfather at all,' he replied. 'I'm merely the recipient of a few confidences. Have you forgotten Nurse Brown?'

'Brown? What's she got to do with it?'

'Possibly nothing, but you yourself told me she had notions of marrying Sir Harry—or was it the other way about?'

She frowned.

'Well, I wouldn't hold it against either of them. Why should I?' she said.

'Even if Fairmile was involved?'

'Why should she care about Fairmile? She once told me that since it was the place I wanted and not the money, that would be a very good compromise—Fairmile for me, and Gramp and his money for any possible candidates. Don't you think that would be a good compromise, Joss?'

He watched her leaning against the trunk of a young fir tree, her hands exploring the smooth bark of the tree, pine

117

needles caught in her hair.

'Oh, Christy!' he exclaimed a little impatiently. 'You are so suspicious when you have no cause, and take so much on trust when you should be cautious. When will you grow up?'

She met his eye, aware of an unexpected stirring of that same excitement she had experienced when he kissed her, and immediately looked away again.

'I don't know that I want to,' she said doubtfully. 'At least—I'm not quite sure what you mean.'

'Aren't you? Well, then, let's play this charming game for a little longer.'

'Game?' she faltered, and he carefully removed the pine needles from her hair.

'Well, let's call it that,' he said. 'Perhaps you need a little longer to get my measure.'

'You confuse me,' she said, and knew to her chagrin that she was disappointed that he had not attempted to follow up his tantalizing suggestions by kissing her.

He had mended the swing for her, making professional knots with new rope and reinforcing the weather-beaten seat with the practised efficiency which had intrigued her while watching him at work on the topiary.

'Why do you bother?' she asked him curiously, but he replied that it was for his own pleasure as much as hers.

'I like to watch you swing and imagine what you were like as a little girl,' he said. 'There's something very innocent and simple about swinging.'

'What a strange man you are,' she said, but she used the mended swing with frank enjoyment. Sometimes he just stood and watched her, lazily appreciative of the slender grace of her body, the flying cloud of her hair, and sometimes he would push her, sending the swing so high that she would know an instant's frisson of fear that she would lose her grip of the ropes and fall out.

'One day,' he told her, 'your children will swing here and the pattern will come full circle.'

'What do you mean? And how do you know that Fairmile will come to me?'

'I don't, but it's the next generation your grandfather has in mind, I think.'

'Of course. But I want children—Gramp knows that.'

'But what he doesn't know is that you have not got a husband,' Joss said gently.

She had been swinging idly while they talked and, at his last remark, she pushed off with too violent an impetus, and slipped from the swing. He caught her neatly and this time he did kiss her as she clung to him in support for a moment. Noakes had lighted a bonfire somewhere, and the bittersweet scent of burning leaves, the tang of autumn in the air and the faint taste of salt on his lips mingled together in sharp delight.

'Joss . . .' she murmured pleadingly, 'I—I couldn't be falling for you, could I?'

He held her at arm's length and his smile was a little crooked.

'Well, now—only you can decide that,' he said with gentle mockery. 'Would I be so bad to cut your teeth on? Lesser men might take advantage, you know.'

'*Lesser* men!' she exclaimed, trying to push him away. 'You have the most devastating knack of spoiling a—a lovely moment.'

'Have I? And don't you think, you perverse little innocent, that I have an end to keep up myself? You lay youself open to unexpected consequences when you pick on a perfect stranger to masquerade as your husband, you know.'

'I'm not your type—you told me so,' she retorted. It was the only retaliation she could think of. He kissed her again, lightly and inconsequently on the tip of her nose, and let her go.

'Propinquity does much to change one's preconceived notions—or haven't you noticed?' he said, and began to whistle.

'What *is* that tune?' she demanded impatiently. 'You're always whistling it.'

'Something remembered from my youth—French-Canadian, I imagine. I forget the name, and only remember two lines.'

'What are they?'

His smile was a little strange.

' "Love is the only charity.
    Pride is the only sin ..."

Worth remembering, wouldn't you think?'

'Yes,' she said, faltering a little at the unexpected seriousness of his observation, and almost at once the casual mockery returned to his eyes. 'Run along back to the house,' he said. 'I have some thinking to do.'

She walked to the house slowly, aware that he was watching her, aware, too, without turning round, of the exact moment when he turned on his heel and walked away.

'Oh hell, oh hell, oh *hell*!' she muttered under her breath. If she was losing her heart to a penniless stranger of whom she knew nothing, her plight would be worse than before. It wasn't fair that he should offer himself so casually as a subject on which to cut her teeth; neither was it fair that, by implication, he had no intention of taking advantage of her.

'And swallow that for a tale!' she told herself more cheerfully, remembering certain other occasions and remarks, and observed with satisfaction as she reached her bedroom that the lock on their communicating door was still without a key.

It was early yet, but she set about changing for the evening with leisurely pleasure, selecting with a critical eye a dress that she thought might please him, wondering if, when he came upstairs, she could casually open the door between their rooms and chat without being misunderstood. But he did not come, and presently she got tired of waiting and went downstairs to see if he had been waylaid by her grandfather.

'Where's everyone?' she asked, finding Sir Harry alone, and he looked up vaguely from the *Times* crossword puzzle, and peered over the top of his reading spectacles.

'Don't know about your good man, but Brown's off duty,' he said.

'Oh, I'd forgotten. Hasn't Joss come in?'

'Not that I know of. Perhaps he's borrowed your car and taken the charming Rose for a spin.'

But she was in no mood for the old man's rather obvious digs.

'Rubbish!' she said quite sharply. 'He said he was going to walk and do some thinking. I'll go and find him.'

'Put something round your shoulders, then, the evenings are getting chilly,' he said without much interest. She went through the hall, snatching up a woollen stole which Brown must have left hanging over the back of a chair, and ran out on to the terrace.

It was the hour when all things are grey; the brilliant colours of leaves and creeper had vanished in the misty stillness of the autumn evening, and little pockets of vapour were rising from the parkland.

Christy was glad the nurse was off duty. She would, she supposed, dine in her room as was her habit, and Christy could have the two men to herself and be gay and charming and very, very adult for Joss's benefit. She walked across lawns drenched with dew, along the twisted paths of the dutch garden, past the topiary, and even peered inside the dusty drag, but she did not find him. She was returning, skirting the maze, when she thought she heard a man's voice. He must, she decided with childish satisfaction, have gone exploring the overgrown maze and got lost; she would indulge in a certain mild pleasure in tracking him down and jeering at the simple failure of that irritating self-sufficiency.

121

The maze had been so neglected that the intricate turns and twists were difficult to follow, but, like Ariadne of old, Christy followed the thread of her own recollection, remembering her mother's tale of the labyrinth of Crete. Suddenly she heard voices. She had, she realized, reached the heart of the maze, and she stood for a moment, uncertainly, with damp seeping through her thin slippers.

'Joss . . .' a soft voice said quite distinctly, '. . . can't we arrive at a compromise?'

His reply was inaudible, but Brown's little sigh of pleasure was quite distinct. She must have moved, probably closer into his arms, Christy thought, for a flash of pale material showed through the dividing hedge. Was he kissing her? But of course he was, with that same, sure treatment which she herself had experienced only that afternoon. After a pause, Brown's voice, still gentle and inviting, observed provocatively:

'You're very strong, aren't you? Strong and silent, like the old-fashioned heroes of fiction, only we all have our breaking point—what's that?'

Christy had turned to run, blundering blindly into branches which caught and tore at the woollen stole she had borrowed.

She must have found her way out of the maze by sheer instinct, for she had no recollection of remembering the half-obliterated landmarks. The stole must have been caught up and left somewhere on a branch, for as she ran across the lawns she realized her shoulders were bare. She almost collided with Tom as she entered the house and, as she fled up the stairs, heard his faintly reproachful voice informing her that drinks were waiting in the study and Sir Harry was getting impatient.

She flopped breathlessly on to her dressing-table stool, kicking off her wet shoes, and regarded her own shocked reflection in the mirror with frank distaste.

122

'Why should I care?' she demanded aloud of herself, but the bitter tears came just the same. For how long had the maze been a trysting place? For how long had Brown called him Joss in private? And how dared he make casual love to herself in the afternoon and go straight to the nurse's arms for a more mature response as soon as her back was turned?

She dabbed more powder on her face, careless of the result, angrily blinked away the tears, and applied unaccustomed mascara which smarted, and, while she was angrily grimacing at herself in the glass, heard Joss go into his room. While she was wildly hunting for another pair of slippers, he unexpectedly opened the communicating door and stood there looking at her.

'What are you doing?' he asked conversationally.

She did not answer but sat down again to put on the fresh pair of slippers.

'Your feet appear to be rather wet,' he observed. 'Have you been out?'

She shot him a glance of fury, then remembered with relief that it was unlikely he had been aware of her presence in the maze.

'Yes,' she replied laconically, and he took another step into the room.

'What have you been doing to your eyes?' he inquired, and ran a finger over her lashes before she could draw back. 'They're wet.'

'Spit,' she snapped, and the corners of his mouth twitched in a smile.

'Oh—mascara,' he said. 'You don't need it, you know. You have the most astonishing dark brows and lashes in contrast with your hair. Hasn't anyone ever told you?'

'Plenty of people. I'm not unused to compliments, you know,' she replied, and was glad to find that armour against him was only a trick. She had merely to go on feeling angry enough and contemptuous enough to give nothing of possible heartache away.

'So you've frequently told me. I prefer you with lashes that aren't all stuck together, all the same.'

'But coming from the backwoods you are, perhaps, unaccustomed to sophisticated make-up. Did you want anything?'

She thought he looked as though he was restraining a desire to laugh, but he only said mildly:

'Not particularly. Why?'

'You don't come into my bedroom as a rule—and you didn't knock.'

'I beg your pardon,' he replied with becoming gravity. 'Well, shall we go down? Your grandpapa is getting somewhat annoyed at being kept waiting.'

'Brown will keep him happy,' she observed, shaking out her full skirt and giving the waistline an impatient tug.

'Nurse Brown will be dining in her room. She's off duty,' he reminded her.

'Oh, is she?' Christy said with devious innocence, and ran out of the room, leaving him to follow.

The evening passed more easily than she had anticipated. She was aware that Joss thought she rather overdid the affectionate granddaughter soothing an old man's irritability by making a blatant fuss of him, but Sir Harry played up as though he was aware that Joss was out of favour and, to Christy at least, it was a relief that Brown absented herself from dinner. She made her excuses early, and left the two men talking. Tom would come as usual to help her grandfather to bed, but by then Christy would be safely in her own bed with no light showing under the door.

She did not sleep well, all the same, and it seemed a long time before she heard Joss moving about next door. Her indignation, the armour which, like a brittle shell, had successfully closed around the greater hurt, had left her, and she knew only a great desire to call to Joss for comfort, to hear him affirm an allegiance which she had no right to expect of him. His light went out very quickly and she lay tossing disconsolately in the big tester bed which had so amused him that first evening.

It was raining when she woke late from troubled, unrefreshing snatches of sleep; not the steady gentle rain which the country was said to need, but the first half-gale of autumn which was already stripping the leaves from the trees and tearing trails of creeper from the walls.

'We must start fires,' Brown said, smiling across the breakfast table at Christy, who experienced such a revulsion of feeling for the nurse that she crammed her mouth full of toast and marmalade to stifle the unconsidered words which might spring to her lips.

Smug, treacherous bitch! she thought, at the same time envying the correct composure with which Brown could address Joss as if nothing lay between them. Only that little trick of suddenly veiling the secret thoughts in her eyes gave her away. There was an added gleam of mockery, too, as she looked at Christy and, as the girl's silence grew, her soft voice took on the indulgent tones which she might have used to humour a sulky child.

'You won't find Fairmile very entertaining if this weather lasts, I'm afraid,' she said, addressing them both, with the absent apology of an attentive hostess. 'You should take Christy to town, Mr. Tavener, and show her a good time. She'll get mopy here.'

'You forget, Brown, that Fairmile happens to be my home,' Christy said with coolness, but the nurse only smiled with unruffled tranquillity.

'Only in the last year, my dear,' she replied. 'You were really more of a stranger here than I was myself—and now, of course, your home is with your husband. When will you be thinking of moving on, Mr. Tavener?'

Joss's lazy eyes rested on her in a long, enigmatic gaze for a moment.

'When I've concluded such business as I've come over here to settle,' he replied suavely, and Christy knew an almost equal hostility for them both; Brown being politely social as if she was indifferent to the ending of an affair with another woman's husband, Joss pretending to conduct business which did not exist.

'We'll leave when I'm ready. Are you in such a hurry to get rid of us?' Christy said with innocent inquiry, and Brown's fine eyebrows rose just a fraction, as if rebuking an impertinence.

'What an odd thing to say. It's scarcely my place to dictate, whatever my wishes, is it?' she replied smoothly.

'No, it isn't,' Christy said, and sent Joss a look which she hoped implied that she was very capable of keeping them both in their appropriate places.

'You sound on edge, Christobel,' Joss remarked with one of his more irritating marital assumptions. 'Perhaps you caught a chill getting your feet so wet on the lawn last night. You weren't at all a restful bedfellow.'

But the old pretence of connubial unity could no longer draw a lively retort from her, and she turned her face away before he could see the pain in her eyes. But Brown saw. She stretched across the table to pat the girl's hand and said lightly:

'Cheer up, Christy! Mr. Fellows is coming for lunch tomorrow; that might mean good news for you, mightn't it?'

'Gramp's lawyer?'

'Yes. Let's hope he won't enrage your grandfather with all his pedantic legal jargon; he's very long-winded. Well, I must see about getting my patient up. Ring for more coffee, won't you, if this has got cold?'

'She behaves as if she was already mistress here,' said Christy crossly as the door gently closed. 'Ring for more coffee, indeed—as if I was a mere guest! Besides, she knows very well that poor old Tom is run off his feet as it is. Don't they always say that nurses make trouble with servants because they won't do a hand's turn themselves?'

She buried her face in her cup of coffee, so did not see Joss's grin as he replied indulgently:

'Now you mustn't be a snob, Christobel dear. That's a very old-fashioned slur on the nursing profession and, in all fairness to our Rose, she's not fussy what she turns her hand to.'

'She certainly isn't!' Christy said with meaning, and banged her cup back into the saucer. 'And speaking of Christian names, how long has she been calling you by yours when no one's around?'

'What do you mean?' he asked casually, but his eyes narrowed.

'Nothing,' she said, and averted her own eyes from his. Nothing was to be gained by blurting out her knowledge of their assignation in the maze when, in point of fact, she herself had no real claim on him.

'You do seem to have got out of bed the wrong side this morning,' he observed conversationally, but there was a new coolness in his voice. 'Will you take a hint from me? Don't antagonize Nurse Brown. I think I've told you that before.'

'Why should I be careful of her feelings? She's not always careful of mine.'

'Possibly not, but she's in a more difficult position than you are.'

'Naturally you would stand up for her!'

'That's childish. I was merely dropping a friendly hint. You don't want things to go wrong before this lawyer chap comes tomorrow, do you?'

'What should go wrong?'

'Well, dear Rose probably has expectations herself, and she has the old man's ear, remember.'

'You mean she'd do me down if she could? Well, that doesn't surprise me.'

'No, I didn't mean that, but I think she means to marry your grandpapa if she can. You always said you didn't care.

Both of them, after all, would accept it as a business arrangement.'

'It's different now,' Christy said, stretching out a hand in mute appeal for a cigarette. 'Snakes are snakes, after all, and she'd want to hang on to Fairmile.'

'Not if you're prepared to compromise, as you once said you were. What's made you so bitter, Christy?'

He had ignored the message of her irritably snapping fingers, but he spoke with kindness. She felt she could no longer trust him, however, if, indeed, she ever had.

'Don't you know?' she retorted, looking him straight in the eye, and saw his mouth tighten.

'I only know that you're behaving like a cross and rather ill-mannered little girl, and I think you must have got a chill from those wet feet after all,' he said, and got up and left the room.

For the rest of that stormy day Christy mooned restlessly about the house, leaving a trail of cigarette ash in her wake. She would have taken her car and driven out to seek more congenial company if she had known where to go, but she realized, for perhaps the first time, what a recluse her grandfather had become. No one called, except the doctor and an occasional local visitor touting for a subscription. The days had gone when social calls and little dinner parties were an accepted way of life, and a new community springing up, with their busy lives and endless domestic complications, had no time for an old man who dwelt in the past and was confined to a wheelchair.

She paused for further reflection in the long, elegant room which once had been the drawing-room. Here, her mother must have presided over charming little At Homes, playing hostess for her father; here, Christy could almost remember being brought down herself by a nanny to be shown off to the visitors, or was she confusing that too with her mother's own childhood?

Joss has spoilt it—Joss and Brown, she thought, going back to the hall to pluck irritably at the moulting feathers of the stuffed peacocks. But Joss was hers, for all the ambiguity of their relationship, and Brown, if she was really scheming to become Lady Tavener, was not going to have him as well.

On this thought she ran up the stairs without further reflection, determined upon action. The weather and her recent discoveries combined to show her that plain speaking was preferable to the nursing of grievances, and, after all, was she not entitled to a showdown which would clear the air?

The nurse always rested in the afternoons, she knew, and as she knocked on Brown's door, she realized with faint surprise that she had seldom been into the room. A voice bade her enter, and as she closed the door behind her she observed with curiosity the changes which had been made. Some of the best pieces of furniture had been moved here, radio and television occupied their respective corners, and the first of the autumn fires already burned in the grate. It was all very comfortable and rather luxurious. Rose Brown lay back in a deep armchair, looking entirely unlike herself in a claret-coloured silk housecoat which Christy had once given her, her hair loose about her shoulders, her feet shod with elegant and absurdly small mules, resting on a low stool.

'Come in,' she said, laying a book face downwards on her knee. 'It isn't often you pay me a visit, Christy. Can I do anything for you?'

Christy stood irresolutely for a moment in the middle of the room, conscious of her own casual slacks and rough jersey. Brown, she supposed, was only relaxing in her off-duty hours, but she presented an unexpected illusion of feminine indolence.

'Can I do anything for you?' she asked again, her face expressing a tolerant tinge of mockery, and Christy's resentment overcame her sense of disadvantage.

'Yes, you can, as a matter of fact,' she said. 'You can stop trying to have an affair with my husband.'

The nurse lowered her lashes for a moment in that secret look of evasion, then she smiled.

'My dear child, how abrupt you are,' she said. 'I haven't an idea what you mean.'

'Oh yes, you have! And to save further beating about the bush I may as well tell you that I came upon the two of you in the maze yesterday.'

Brown gave a little yawn.

'Did you? Well, that accounts for my stole. I suppose you borrowed it.'

'Yes, I did, but——'

'Joss found it caught on a branch. He must have wondered. It's not a very nice habit, spying, Christy.'

Christy replied with an unconscious echo of her grandfather's manner:

'I was not spying, Brown. You should have realized that since this is my home I have the freedom of the place, and taken the necessary precautions. Do you and Joss often meet there?'

'My dear girl,' Brown said, a tinge of boredom in her voice, 'why can't you be your age? I understood you prided yourself on your independence and the modern outlook. A mild extra-marital pass or two shouldn't worry you.'

Christy's dislike of the nurse could now be plainly seen in the cool contempt in her clear eyes, and she shook back her hair impatiently.

'I'm not *that* modern,' she retorted. 'And I won't stand for this sort of thing under my own roof.'

'It's not your roof—yet, my dear,' Brown said with silky gentleness.

'Perhaps not, but it's my grandfather's and you're his employee. Gramp may be casual and given to crude humour at times, but he, no more than I, would stand for any

130

funny business between his nurse and my husband. You don't want me to give him a hint, do you?'

'I shouldn't think you would, since Joss isn't your husband,' Brown replied calmly, and smiled a little cruelly as she saw the unguarded look of alarm flash over the girl's face.

'You aren't really in a very strong position to dictate, are you?' she added softly.

Christy stood very straight and slender, her clenched hands thrust into the pockets of her slacks.

'Why do you say that?' she demanded coldly in a naïve attempt to brazen things out, but the nurse only laughed.

'Oh, come now!' she said. 'You don't really think I believed that ridiculous story from the start, do you?'

'You fostered the story very prettily—even to getting Gramp to accept the situation.'

'Well, it was your way out of a difficulty, wasn't it? It may have been a foolish impulse, but I couldn't altogether blame you. Besides, I had fish of my own to fry.'

Christy turned to the window and watched the rain streaming ceaselessly down the panes. The park looked desolate and sodden, and the untended potholes in the long avenue held an endless chain of puddles.

'You thought with me out of the way you'd catch Gramp more easily, didn't you?' she said, and although her back was turned she could picture the politely raised eyebrows as the nurse replied rather coolly:

'Isn't that a little vulgar? I'm not out to catch anyone— neither your grandfather nor your so-called husband.'

Christy swung round, her temper out of control. How dared this woman patronize her and treat her like an ill-mannered child! She was too young and inexperienced, for all her boasting, to fence with words; she could only retaliate with adolescent rudeness, which fact Joss had very early on discovered.

'You needn't play the lady of the manor with me, Rose

Brown,' she snapped. 'You're not mistress here yet, and when my grandfather discovers what kind of woman you are, I doubt if you ever will be.'

'And what should he discover? That Joss has been paying me a little more attention than was proper? Your grandfather's a man of the world, my dear. I hardly think that would be held against me.'

Her calm complacency was infinitely galling, and Christy knew a most uncharacteristic desire to hurt and hurt cruelly.

'What he wouldn't hold against an employee who allows a guest to amuse himself with her, he'd scarcely tolerate in his future wife,' she said, and this time the shaft went home. Brown's eyes narrowed unpleasantly and her mouth tightened at the corners.

'Very well,' she said, 'if you want to play it that way then we know where we stand. If you care to tell tales then I have one of my own that will soon put the sly little granddaughter in the soup. How do you think Sir Harry will feel when he finds out you've made a fool of him? What chance do you imagine you will ever have of getting your precious Fairmile once he knows he's been tricked?'

She had broken her studied pose of indolence now, and leant forward in the chair, her hands clenched on her knee; strong hands, ruthless hands, which Christy watched helplessly, knowing now the strength and determination which lay beneath the other woman's soft, demure demeanour.

'That sounds like blackmail,' Christy said, her chin up. 'My secret kept in exchange for yours.'

'Blackmail's an ugly word,' Rose Brown said. 'And after all, my poor little misdemeanour is scarcely comparable to yours. Even if you should be so rash as to tell tales, there's no harm done by having a few moments of dalliance with an attractive stranger on whom neither you nor your grandfather has any claim. Think again, Christy—you're the only one who stands to lose.'

The room was growing darker as the light outside began

to fade. Firelight patterned the walls with a cosy intimacy that seemed entirely false; there was no warmth, no certainty left in the day.

'And do you imagine my grandfather wouldn't demand an explanation as to why you had connived at the deception?' Christy asked.

'I should deny it, of course. There's no possible proof that I ever doubted your marriage. I paved the way for you much too well for that.'

'And have you told Joss you know the truth?'

Brown gave a little shrug.

'My dear girl, in my profession, discreetness is one of the first maxims one has to learn,' she replied. 'Have you, in your turn, taxed him with being unfaithful?'

'No.'

'Wise girl. Don't do it. You're rather fond of him, aren't you? Funny if this little prank of yours is going to boomerang.'

'I don't know what you mean.'

'Don't you? I think you've fallen for him.'

'You can think what you damn well please!' Christy retaliated, driven to plain rudeness. The nurse smiled and leant back again in her chair.

'Poor Christy!' she said. 'You've picked a tough proposition for your first experiment in romance, haven't you? It *is* your first?'

'Why should you imagine that?'

'You're so transparent. This pose you had of self-sufficiency, independence, modern frankness—it didn't deceive me. Perhaps you don't realize you've changed. It's a pity you had to pick your hired assassin to cut your teeth on.'

Cutting her teeth, the innocent milk-teeth of inexperience ... hadn't Joss himself suggested, with gentle mockery, that he could be a good subject on which to experiment because lesser men might take advantage?

'Why?' she asked, because the simple question seemed

133

important and she was too honest to save her face by denial.

'Because, my dear, he is scarcely a man with honourable intentions. You should make the most of those adjoining rooms of your—or perhaps you already have.'

'You're disgusting!' Christy cried, longing to slap that smooth, mocking face. 'Disgusting and cheap! You may be content with a tumble in the hay with a man you know nothing about, but I'm not. Don't, please, judge me by your own standards—or Joss's.'

The nurse sprang to her feet and swiftly administered the slap which Christy had itched to deliver.

'You think I'm cheap and disgusting, do you?' she bit back, losing her self-control at last. 'What do you know about the way the other half lives? How do you imagine it feels to accept with a show of gratitude gifts of cast-off clothing, perfume—any unwanted small luxury that costs nothing to give? Oh, you're generous, maybe, Christy, in a careless, patronising fashion, but you are, after all, only a rather silly little chit of a girl who's allowed a bit of money and independence to go to her head. Did you think you could buy Joss, too?'

As Brown's bitter venom spilled out, Christy felt suddenly emptied of anger. She could never like this woman or forgive her for her treachery, but she was genuinely shocked that her own well-intentioned actions had only resulted in bitterness.

'Brownie,' she said, reverting unconsciously to her former affectionate mode of address, 'I never meant to patronize. I'm sorry if I hurt you, but—but I liked you once.'

'As you'd like any sycophant who humbly admired and was willing to perform small services. I've met your kind before,' Brown said with rough contempt, and Christy flushed.

'I wasn't to know what you thought of me, was I?' she replied with gentle dignity. 'Neither does the fact that you dislike me excuse your present attitude. It will be very much better for everyone if I make a clean breast of things to my grandfather.'

'Will it? Think again, my dear. Who's going to come out of this best? My own part in this affair will only be vindicated by the absurd accusations of a jealous little girl. Sir Harry is scarcely likely to run me off because I, like him, was grossly deceived.'

It was unanswerable, of course. Christy had, in an unthinking moment of folly, made her own bed, and now the trap had sprung. No good going to Gramp to sort out the mess, no good confiding in Joss who, for all she knew, might have more than a passing fancy for Rose Brown.

'Very well,' she said. 'What is it you want of me?'

'Simply to go on playing your part. After tomorrow, all our ways may be clear.'

'You mean to marry Gramp, don't you?'

'And if I do, why should you care? Things would go on exactly as before, the only difference being that I would have a position—security for the future. Do you grudge me that?'

'No. But what of Fairmile?'

'Ah—Fairmile ...' Brown muttered, turning away to plump up cushions, empty ashtrays, all the little automatic services which had been natural to her for so long. 'I don't want Fairmile, if my settlement's good enough. This place would be an encumbrance and a tomb for a widow. No, Christy, you can keep Fairmile, if that's in Sir Harry's mind for the future, but remember—if you try to spoil my game, I'll spoil yours. Now, hadn't we better call a truce?'

A truce, thought Christy, after all the things that had been said!

'What did you mean by buying Joss?' she asked, still in that uncertain state of wanting her i's dotted and her t's crossed.

'Only that you've picked the wrong man. He doesn't

135

need money.'

Christy remembered that he had given her grandfather the same impression, and said sharply:

'Joss hasn't any money. He lives by his wits, so don't run away with the idea that he'll be good for a spot of your blackmail.'

The nurse threw another log on the fire and watched the flame leap up with a little smile.

'Really?' she said. 'Well, his wits must have been sharp enough to see him through Charterhouse and a university. Don't you know anything about him, my dear?'

'Less than you, presumably,' Christy replied, adding with innocent pleasure, 'But perhaps he's led you up the garden as well as Gramp. Don't believe all the tales Joss spins, will you, Brown? I wouldn't like to think you were labouring under a misapprehension.'

The nurse looked at her and, for a moment, there seemed to be a conflict of exasperation and pity in her expression.

'Oh, go away,' she said impatiently. 'Go and find this come-by-chance of yours and treat him to some of the nonsense I've been hearing. You won't find him a very sympathetic audience, though, I warn you.'

CHAPTER SEVEN

CHRISTY ran down the stairs and out of the house, only pausing to snatch a raincoat from the big press in the hall as she went. The rain beat in her face as she struggled against the wind, and she had passing thoughts of wood fires and crumpets for tea, and the pleasant indolence of an afternoon confined to the house by the weather. But anything was better than being boxed up with three people none of whom she could any longer depend on for support. Presently the very wildness of the day seemed a fitting accompaniment to her mood and, although soon she was not only buffeted but soaked, the bitterness and anger and bewilderment began to die out of her.

Go on playing your part, Brown had said. Well, there was nothing else to do, but the thought of her grandfather troubled her. She had known him barely a year and their relationship had gone no deeper than the surface value of daily bickering and mutual appreciation, but she had come to love him, despite their differences, and she did not care any more for the deception which she had so lightheartedly practised on him. Of Joss she refused to think at all. He had been willing to be hired on terms which she now realized the average decent man would have thought twice about before accepting; if he chose to amuse himself elsewhere in the meantime, he was scarcely to be blamed. It was a pity that she herself should have become emotionally involved, for, as Brown had pointed out, he seemed hardly a man of honourable intentions. Still, one must take the rough with the smooth, Christy argued with herself severely, then sat suddenly down on a nearby fallen tree to weep.

She sat for a long time, crying and cursing by turn, and

wet and slime from the saturated log seeped through to her very skin, while the shoes she had not thought to change were waterlogged and the thin leather reduced to pulp. It began to get dark and she got up to start for home, aware that she was stiff in every limb and rather cold. Well, the nurse had certainly won the first round, she admitted to herself rather grimly, and when finally she reached the grounds and knew herself reluctant to go in and face them all, she slipped into the coach-house and climbed into the old drag where, as a child, she had not only played at highwaymen, but hidden from the just wrath of a much-tried nanny.

The rotting upholstery smelt fustier than ever with the damp, but she curled up gratefully on the ancient cushions, confident that no one would find her, and fell asleep.

It was quite dark when she woke, thinking she had heard someone calling her, and almost at once a door of the drag was wrenched open and a man's head and shoulders appeared out of the gloom.

'For crying out loud!' Joss's voice exclaimed angrily. 'Have you been here all the afternoon? I've been looking for you everywhere.'

'No,' she said, feeling she had been caught at a dis-advantage, her thoughts still confused. 'I've been walking.'

He groped for her in the darkness, feeling the sodden dampness of her slacks, and then climbed in beside her to run his hands over her wet head.

'Good grief, child! What possessed you to stay here when you're soaked to the skin?' he exclaimed and, when she did not answer, took her face between his hands, warm and reassuring to her chilled flesh.

'Hiding, weren't you—like when you were a little girl?' he said, and for all her bitter disillusionment, she still wanted to rest her head on his breast and be comforted.

'Yes,' she whispered. 'Brown and I had words. I—I was upset.'

138

'Brown?' he echoed a little sharply, and she thought he withdrew a little. Of course, it was hardly tactful, or wise, to mention the nurse. 'What did you have words about?'

'Nothing,' she murmured, and he gave a short little laugh which held no amusement.

'One can scarcely have words about nothing,' he observed, 'though possibly two women can. However, that's of little importance. You're shivering.'

Indeed, her teeth were beginning to chatter, and without more ado, he bundled her unceremoniously out of the drag and ran her back to the house. Tom had lighted a great fire of logs in the hall. She looked longingly at the leaping flames, but Joss dragged her relentlessly up the staircase and into her room.

'Get out of those wet things at once. I'll run you a bath,' he said, but she was still standing in the middle of the room gazing down at her drowned reflection in the glass when he returned.

'For heaven's sake!' he exclaimed, and started peeling the wet clothes off her. She made one feeble protest, but he paid no attention, and soon she was standing naked and shivering while he hunted through her wardrobe for a dressing-gown.

'Don't let me embarrass you,' he remarked as he wrapped it round her. 'A husband has a perfect right to remove his wife's clothes.'

'*Oh!*' she cried, immediately touched on the raw, and began to cry.

'Christy . . .' He sounded concerned, and his fingers were gentle as he tilted her face up to his. 'What's upset you? I can't always resist teasing, but you may weep on my manly chest with pleasure if it will bring any comfort.'

She would like to have done just that, but she remembered Brown, and remembered, too, that he had offered himself, with careless indifference, as a willing subject on which to cut her teeth.

'No, thank you,' she replied, wriggling out of his grasp. 'I'll have that bath if it's ready for me.'

He accompanied her firmly to the bathroom and tested the water carefully.

'Perhaps I'd better stay. You seem to be in a peculiar state and might drown,' he said, and she pushed him towards the door in alarm. He was, she knew, quite capable of carrying out the threat.

'I certainly won't drown,' she snapped, and sneezed convulsively.

'I'll turn my back,' he promised gravely, and, too late, she caught the familiar grin he employed when he had got a rise. She started to reply, but was interrupted by another sneeze, and he remarked severely before he closed the door behind him :

'Tiresome brat! Now I suppose you'll have me up half the night administering hot possets and soothing poultices.' It was only when she was soaking blissfully in the warm water that she wondered whether it was from tact or more personal reasons that he had refrained from suggesting Rose Brown as the obvious person to offer professional attention, if required.

He came back as she was finishing dressing, with a strong hot toddy, and remained sitting on the side of the bed watching her comb out her still damp hair. She was scarcely looking her best, she thought crossly, aware that despite her mixed feelings, it was pleasant to have him occupying the room as if he belonged there. She was, she realized wryly, in for a really stinking cold.

'That'll have to do,' she observed, favouring her reflection with a final disgusted look. 'Joss, were you really at Charterhouse?'

His eyebrows lifted in quizzical inquiry.

'Yes. Does that surprise you?'

'It does rather. Why didn't you tell me?'

'You never asked.'

140

'But you told Brown.'

'Nurse Brown has shown rather more interest in my background than you.'

'Why don't you call her Rose?'

'Rose, then, if you like. Were you quarrelling about me, by any chance?'

'Certainly not!' she replied sharply, and wished with disconsolate forlornness that he had not made it impossible for her to tell him the whole sorry story.

'What a pity,' he countered calmly. 'I should like to think I could rouse a little jealousy in you.'

'That, of course, would be typical,' she snapped. 'You're probably the sort of man who would enjoy having two women fighting over you.'

'How do you know what sort of man I am?' he inquired, unmoved, and suddenly grinned. 'Fine! I've made you good and angry again. That's better than wallowing in a mess of self-pity, isn't it? Let's go down.'

'I do *not* wallow in self-pity!' she exclaimed, hastening with alacrity across the room. 'What have I got to be sorry about, anyhow?'

'What indeed,' he replied innocently, and gave her behind a gentle slap as she whisked past him through the door.

She did her best to appear as usual throughout the evening, determined to give Rose Brown no cause for satisfaction, but it proved to be a losing battle. She felt feverish and shivery, could scarcely touch the food put down before her and relapsed, finally, into a most unusual silence.

'Cat got your tongue?' Sir Harry inquired rather irritably, and only frowned impatiently when she tried to reply with the familiar flippant nonsense. He, it seemed, was also feeling under the weather and complained frequently of the headaches which had troubled him lately with greater frequency. Every so often the nurse gave him a quick, professional glance, a little frown creasing her smooth forehead, but when Joss suggested casually that it might be a good idea to postpone the lawyer's visit the next day, she did not immediately second the proposal.

'I think Sir Harry will feel happier once his affairs are settled,' she said carefully, intercepting, with a faint smile, the look which Christy sent her which said plainly enough that it was Brown who would feel happier once her own future was assured.

'You look as if you're running a temperature, Christy,' she said. 'Have you caught cold?'

'It seems fairly obvious that I've caught cold,' snapped Christy, who had been sneezing for the best part of the evening, and Brown rose at once, saying she would fetch her thermometer.

In common with a great many other people, Christy disliked having her temperature taken under the curious eyes of others. She felt helpless and rather foolish with the thermometer stuck in her mouth while Brown took her pulse and studied the seconds hand of her watch.

'A hundred and one,' she pronounced. 'You'd getter get to bed. What made you go out and get soaking wet on a day like this?'

'As if you didn't know!' Christy replied, scarcely above a whisper, but Joss heard and she thought he exchanged a fleeting look of commiseration with the nurse.

'You're both of you——' she began on a rising note of hysteria, but he interrupted her to say firmly:

'Now, darling, think before you burst into unconsidered speech. Temperatures of a hundred and one are apt to distort the reason. Off to bed. In due course I'll bring up the hot posset to which I was already resigned.'

'I'll see to that, Mr. Tavener. There's no need for you to have a broken night,' Brown said, and merely raised reproving eyebrows when Christy protested with a violent 'No!'

'You have your own patient to attend to, Nurse Brown. I'm quite competent to deal with my wife's requirements,'

Joss interposed with unexpected partisanship, and Christy saw the quick look of surprise in the nurse's eyes.

'As you wish,' she replied a little shortly. 'You'd better keep her in bed tomorrow. She's evidently got a thorough chill. Now, Sir Harry, what about saying good night? Your head's bothering you again, isn't it?'

'Yes, it bloody well *is*!' the old man snapped with the indignant rudeness of a child who has been left out of the limelight too long. 'All this fuss about a common or garden cold! For God's sake take Brown's advice and stay in bed tomorrow, Christy, and don't go spreading germs all over the house!'

'No one,' said Christy, trying at the last to gather round her the scattered remnants of cool indifference, 'need trouble about my cold. I have aspirin, and a hot-water bottle and my bed are all I want. I'll lock my door, Joss, so you won't be disturbed. Good night.'

'It has no key,' he reminded her innocently, and she thought she saw Brown give a wry little smile which held no amusement.

Christy dragged herself wearily up to bed. Her head ached violently and she longed for the relief of an irrational fit of crying. The marble staircase struck cold to her feet and the wind had found hidden cracks and inlets in the old house to send unwelcome draughts whistling down the corridors. She shivered, dwelling on the rather gloomy chill of her bedroom, but when she reached it an unexpected welcome awaited her. Someone had lighted the fire since dinner, two hot water bottles were in the bed and a thermos flask and a mug set ready on a tray beside it.

Tom ... Mrs. Heap ... Brown? But the servants had not known she had a cold and Brown would scarcely have troubled after their scene of the afternoon. Joss, then? Almost at once she saw the sheet of notepaper propped against the thermos. He had written: *Warm your poor little bones and don't prop a chair under the door-handle. I'll be along*

143

later with a cup of cold poison.

She began to cry then, with a mixture of fever and gratitude, realizing that despite the polite attentions which money could always buy, this was the first time since her mother had died that someone had gratuitously thought of the small, personal expressions of solace for her comfort.

Her temperature must have risen, for Joss found her, later, tossing and still weeping in the big bed, the blankets pushed back.

'Hey, there...' he said softly. 'This won't do. Cover yourself up, child, and sweat it out. Why are you crying?'

'I don't know ... I feel ill ... and you lighted the fire and put b-bottles in my bed, didn't you? It was so k-kind....'

'Well, no one else seemed to have had the notion. Why should that upset you?'

'Because it was a—a spontaneous gesture and not paid for.'

'My poor Christy ... has no one ever shown you loving kindness without hope of reward?' he asked with a mixture of amusement and tenderness, and firmly put the bedclothes back, tucking them tightly around her.

'I suppose so, only—well, there hasn't been anybody who minded much in the last year. You don't really mind, do you? I'm so hot,' she said, trying, without much avail, to push the bedclothes off again.

'If you thought I didn't mind then there was no cause to weep.'

'Wasn't there? But perhaps I wanted you to. Either way it could make one cry, couldn't it?'

'I wouldn't know,' he replied a little brusquely, and laid a cool hand on her forehead, gently pushing back the damp hair. 'No, Christy—you're to keep wrapped up, however hot you may feel. I'll go and get that cup of cold poison now. It will bring your temperature down.'

It seemed to Christy that for most of the night he was in and out of her room. He must have acquired a spirit lamp from somewhere, for he brought a succession of hot drinks, pushed pills down her throat and even changed her night-dress when it became wet with sweat. It was extraordinarily comforting to find him standing by the bed, unfamiliar but homely in pyjamas and dressing-gown. In the confusing distortions of fever she could almost believe that he really was her husband, someone in whom it would be natural to confide the distressing events of the day; but if he had married her and was conducting an affair with another woman, then there was nothing to be gained by accusing that same woman and laying oneself open to a snub.

'Oh dear ... what a muddle it all is ...' she murmured distractedly, and felt his hand on her forehead again, smoothing, soothing. The callouses on his fingers had almost vanished with the weeks of idleness, she noticed with faint surprise, and was too tired to complain when he slipped an arm round her shoulders, propping her up for yet another draught of medicine.

'Did you pinch all this stuff from Brown?' she asked, and he grinned down at her.

'Oh no. We have to carry our own first-aid kit in the backwoods. It's a rough life and no amenities.'

'I don't believe you ever roughed it in the backwoods at all,' she said.

'Don't you? But it was your idea in the first place.'

'Yes, but—the orphanage part. Was that true?'

'Oh yes, that was true,' he replied a little grimly. 'Now stop asking questions and try to get some sleep. I could do with some myself.'

She reached up a hand to touch his chin which, in the small hours, was beginning to look in need of a shave. As the lamplight caught a faint gleam in the stubble she remembered noticing that day they had first met that were he to grow a beard it would be grey.

'How odd,' she murmured drowsily. 'There's no grey in your hair.'

'I dye my hair. The beard's a giveaway,' he told her gravely, and she gave a weak giggle.

Towards dawn the fever broke and she did sleep, aware, as she slipped into unconsciousness, that the door between their rooms stood open for the first time and that she only had to call to bring Joss back. It was a comforting thought on which to embrace the dreamless sleep of exhaustion.

It was past midday when she woke to find the rain still beating against the window and Brown standing beside the bed, thermometer in hand.

'Well,' the nurse said with a hint of irony, 'you should have worked it out of your system by now.'

Christy was about to inquire whether there was a double meaning in that remark, but Brown thrust the thermometer into her mouth, rendering her temporarily speechless.

'Not very thoughtful of you, was it, to go courting pneumonia out of sheer ill temper?' Brown observed pleasantly. 'However, it was one way of drawing attention to yourself, I suppose. I hope Joss rose to the occasion.'

Christy uttered wordless sounds of indignation and was about to remove the thermometer when the nurse lightly slapped her hand down.

'Another half-minute, please. Poor Christy—he disappointed you, did he? *I* could have told you that he merely regards you as a spoilt little ninny whose game he was prepared to play for the time being because it happened to suit his book.'

'What do you mean by happening to suit his book?' Christy demanded as soon as she could speak again.

'Work it out for yourself. Didn't you once tell me he lived by his wits?' the nurse replied calmly. 'I hope you were discreet if you had any lightheaded moments in the might, Christy, I warned you he wasn't the type to spill love's awakening all over the place. He likes his women

146

more mature. Your temperature's down, but you look rather washed out. You'd better stay where you are for the rest of the day.'

She had dropped her hints in exactly the same tone of voice in which she had proffered her professional opinion, and Christy watched her calm face as she took down the thermometer and wondered uneasily just how much she might have confided to Joss during the night. She had only a vague impression of his frequent comings and goings, of half-remembered tenderness and her own desire for comfort. But he had not kissed her, nor had he encouraged confidences or explanations. For all his amusement that she should admit to being grateful because his attentions had been offered without hope of reward, did not his unexpected consideration spring exactly from that? If one is being paid five hundred pounds for a few weeks of easy living, a small amount of simulated concern is hardly much to expect.

'Oh hell, oh hell, oh buckets of *blood*!' she exclaimed, thumping her pillows with violence as Brown went away, gently closing the door. The solace of the night had gone, the tangle of her own creating no nearer solution, and Joss and Brown ... Joss and Rose Brown, whatever their respective feelings for each other, were working against her for their own ends. ...

He looked in to see her just before luncheon, bringing her a glass of champagne. The lawyer had already arrived, he said, and Sir Harry had grudgingly produced a vintage wine to fortify himself against a tedious afternoon.

'Funny little dried-up blighter, not approving, I rather gather, of his client's change of heart. Gave me a thoroughly old-fashioned look on being introduced.' Joss said.

'That should hardly surprise you,' Christy replied coldly. She had forgotten about Mr. Fellows. 'Gramp has had fortune-hunters on the brain ever since he took me back into

147

the fold.'

'So you've frequently told me. Well, we shall have to wait and see whether the fact that I seem to be approved of has helped your little scheme.'

'It wasn't only Fairmile that made me tell such lies,' she said a little pleadingly. 'He wanted to marry me off to some ghastly relation he'd never met just because his name was Tavener.'

'Ah yes, the Northumbrian gentleman. Still, if I know you, Christy, you wouldn't have allowed yourself to be forced into marriage unless your passion for acquiring Fairmile was such an obsession that you'd stop at nothing.'

She thought she detected a hint of asperity behind the lightness of his words, and said sharlply:

'I've *told* you—I didn't think! I just said the first thing that came into my head, and you shouldn't judge others by yourself, Joss Tavener. *You* may be the kind that would stop at nothing, but I have—have certain standards.'

'Have you, indeed? Ah well, our positions are a little different. You've been raised soft while I've had to battle for my small successes—with or without standards.'

'What do you mean—your small successes? And you haven't asked me how I am this morning.'

One eyebrow lifted quizzically.

'No need,' he said. 'I can see you're quite yourself, except for an unbecoming cold.'

'That's not very gallant. I dare say my nose *is* red, and my eyes watering.'

'Not red—just slightly pink at the tip. Don't drink that champagne so fast; it will make you hiccup.'

'I hope,' she said, sounding suddenly tearful, 'that I pass my stinking cold on to you! You won't be so superior and pleased with yourself when you're all bunged up and sneezing every m-minute.'

Even as she spoke she sneezed again herself, and he replied, shaking his head reproachfully:

'There's gratitude for you, after tending to your needs half the night and losing my beauty sleep!'

She gave him a little wavering smile of apology, drank the last mouthful of champagne, and held out the empty glass.

'I'm sorry,' she said. 'You were very kind and—and considerate. I could have told you things then.'

'Perhaps you did,' he replied, taking the glass from her, and her dark lashes flew up in a look of alarm.

'What things?' she asked quickly, thinking not of Rose Brown and the trouble she had made, but of her own weak surrender to his attentions. Had she, in her lightheaded moments, embarrassed him by confessing again to her suspicions as to the state of her heart, and, if not, could she keep up the familiar bickering until their contract expired so that he should never guess?

The long sigh she gave was more heartfelt than she knew. He stood for a moment looking down at her in silence, while he twirled the glass idly round in his fingers.

'Nothing that mattered—nothing that, perhaps, I didn't know already,' he said then. 'How small you look in that vast bed. It's a pity that two such aggressively connubial couches such as yours and mine should be wasting their potentialities, isn't it? I'll be back later, when the lawyer chap has gone.'

Mrs. Heap came up presently with a tray and stayed to lay and light the fire, and enjoy a gossip at the same time. Mr. Fellows' visit was clearly a matter of some moment in the kitchen, and the cook was filled with excited curiosity and an air of being in the know.

'Tom and me is in the will, and Noakes too, which is only right seeing how long we've all been in the old gentleman's service, but you never know, do you?' she said.

'And how do you know now?'

' 'Cos we're none of us called to witness. That's the law, miss; legatees can't witness the will. The two daily girls are wanted after lunch, so that means Nurse Brown can expect something, and it goes without saying that you, as the only grandchild, will come in for a fair share. Exciting, isn't it?'

'Not very,' Christy replied, experiencing a sudden distaste for the whole business. It was natural enough, she supposed, for there to be speculation below stairs, and old Tom and Mrs. Heap and Noakes were entitled to expectations, but Brown hoping for money and position, and she herself scheming for Fairmile, began to sicken her.

Mrs. Heap, making a great clatter with coal and fire-irons, paused to rest her large behind on her heels.

'Well, not for you, maybe, miss,' she said, sounding a little huffy. 'Your prospects are a certainty, as you might say, and a fine man to support you into the bargain.'

'Nothing's a certainty, Mrs. Heap. Things can go wrong,' Christy said, sounding suddenly tired, and the fat cook looked remorseful.

'There! What am I thinking of, talking like this with the old gentleman still alive and all, and you with that nasty cold enough to give anyone thoughts of the grave. I don't like lawyers in the house and that's a fact—smell of death they do. That's a pretty bed-jacket you're wearing, Miss Christy—is it the one Mr. Joss brought you from London?'

Christy glanced down at the rather bedraggled garment with disfavour. It was, indeed, the present Joss had brought her, chosen, he said, by Brown. It was, Christy had thought, just the sort of thing Brown would choose for someone else—thin and cheap, machine-knitted and of an unbecoming colour.

'It isn't really very nice. Nurse Brown chose it,' she said, and Mrs. Heap chuckled.

'Trust a man to get his shopping down by another woman! Still and all, Nurse Brown wasn't to know she could have spread herself. She couldn't have afforded better for herself,' she said, and Christy regarded her with faint surprise. She herself had such a very different picture of

150

Rose Brown that it was strange to realize that the servants accepted her at face value, affording her respect and a possible tolerance because she saved them work and did not give herself airs.

'No, I suppose not,' Christy said, and added slowly: 'Mrs. Heap, would you and Tom be surprised if—if Nurse Brown should ever become mistress here?'

The cook lighted the fire and paused to blow at the flames before answering, then she struggled to her feet, her cheeks scarlet with the effort.

'Why, bless you, no, miss,' she said. 'Quite the thing, old gentlemen marrying their nurses, I'm told. Well, it's sensible, both sides, isn't it? Once your nurse is your wife, she can't up and leave you for another job, can she? Sir Harry's often said that very thing.'

'My grandfather's said it to you?'

'Only joking-like, of course. We've often discussed it in the kitchen. Tom don't hold with the notion much—calls the nurse a scheming hussy, but he's a man. Doesn't understand when a woman's not getting any younger she has to look after her future.'

'Then you'd stop on?' Christy said, her heart warming to the more uncharitable Tom.

'Why not? Too old to make a change now. Besides, things wouldn't be no different.'

Oh, wouldn't they! Christy said to herself. Brown had been clever never giving cause for friction where the servants were concerned, but Christy thought she wouldn't mind betting that once the new Lady Tavener had control of the reins, she would not tolerate for very long the scamped work of old servants who had too much to do.

When the cook had taken away the tray, Christy tried a cigarette, but it did not taste very nice and she stubbed it out. She dozed for a little, but she could not rest for long. Her thoughts were focused too uncomfortably on this momentous signing of the will. Brown's machinations could not really hurt her grandfather, even if she succeeded in marrying him, for he was too tough a proposition to become wax in the hands of any woman, but Christy's own deceit, and Joss's, were another matter. She could not take Fairmile under false pretences, even had he decided to leave the place to her, but neither could she confess, now things had gone so far, for, much as she distrusted the nurse, she could not afford to ignore those hints and warnings and risk the shock which might prove fatal.

'But I can stop it—I can reject the whole idea!' she said aloud, and already had both legs over the side of the bed. Only a sudden vision of the lawyer's outraged face should she follow her first impulse and appear among them in her nightdress kept her from doing just that. Instead she ran down the corridor which led to the gallery and, leaning far out over the balustrade, called loudly for Joss.

Her hoarse voice echoed round the gallery, and she did not stop shouting until she saw him come running across the hall, looking up at her with a startled expression.

'For heaven's sake, what's the matter?' he demanded as he reached her at the top of the stairs. 'You look as white as a ghost—couldn't you have rung a bell?'

'Perhaps I've been seeing ghosts,' she said breathlessly. 'Nothing's the matter—well, yes, there is, really. Joss, I have to tell you something. It's very important.'

'For heaven's sake!' he exclaimed, observing her bare feet and transparent nightdress and his despised present which was her only other covering. 'You weren't thinking of coming downstairs like that, were you?'

'Yes, I was, then I thought I'd better call you instead.'

'I should hope so! Do you want to catch pneumonia on top of that chill?' he said, and picked her up without more ado and carried her back to her room.

'Now,' he said, having deposited her none too gently in the bed, 'what's this vital information that you couldn't

152

wait another minute to impart?'

'I had to catch you before they signed the will. When I've told you, you can tell them and then it'll be all right,' she said, not very lucidly.

He saw the two high spots of colour in her cheekbones and the brightness of her eyes, and sat down on the side of the bed, taking her hands in a firm, reassuring grasp.

'You're running up that temperature again,' he said. 'Try to think calmly and tell me what you want to, then I'll give you something to put you to sleep.'

'Have you been a doctor among all your other trades?' she asked, and give a small, rather nervous giggle.

'No.'

'Well, perhaps a vet?'

'No,' he said, and smiled reassuringly. 'I'm waiting, Christy. What do you want to tell me?'

But it was not easy to begin, to lead up logically to the decision she had come to, so, characteristically, she plunged baldly in at the end.

'I don't want Fairmile,' she said a little feverishly, 'I want you to go downstairs and tell Gramp not to make any changes in his will. Tell him—tell him it was all a mistake. Tell him I'll be living in Canada—tell him anything—make something up.'

His eyes held a curious expression. For a moment it was almost as if he had expected to hear something else and was disappointed, but disappointment, if indeed it was that, gave place to grave inquiry.

'You don't want Fairmile?' he repeated slowly. 'But hasn't that been the object of all this play-acting nonsense?'

'Yes, of course, but don't you see, Joss, it didn't start out as—as a deliberate deception. I—I never expected Gramp to believe the story once he'd had time to think about it, and if Brown hadn't——'

'If Brown hadn't what?'

His question had a sudden sharpness and she remembered that she had no means of knowing how much or how little he and the nurse might be in each other's confidence.

'Nothing, really,' she said quickly. 'But she persuaded him to accept my—my mythical husband before I had time to tell him it wasn't true, and I was stuck with the story. Since we've been here, things have got worse and worse. Gramp won't stand for divorce.'

His smile was a little ironical.

'So you've discussed that already, have you? You really do rush your fences, don't you, Christy? You could scarcely expect the old boy to take a favourable view of divorce when you're supposed to be a bride of only a month or two's standing!'

She rummaged under her pillows for a handkerchief and blew her nose with violence.

'It was a misunderstanding, actually,' she said. 'I'd been sounding him out, you see, and when I saw I'd put my foot in it I suddenly got sickened of the whole thing and was going to make a clean breast of everything, but he wouldn't listen, thinking I was still talking about a divorce. He just flew into a passion and said I was jealous.'

'Jealous?'

'It was the day you had taken Brown to London.'

'Oh, I see. And were you jealous?'

'That,' she said, withdrawing coldly, 'is neither here nor there. The point is I—I don't want Fairmile under false pretences, and I want you to go down and tell them so.'

He sat with his arms folded and regarded her in silence for a moment or two. She did not altogether care for the way he was looking at her, nor did she understand the expression in his eyes.

'You *can* do that, Joss, can't you?' she asked a little anxiously. 'You—you can tell him I will explain, myself, when I'm well again. I—I'll make things all right for you, too. I'll tell him I persuaded you and you needed the money but everything was quite above-board.'

154

'Friendly persuasion?' he said gently. 'Do you think that's the way he will look at it?'

'Of course, once I've explained. I *am* persuasive, you know—he might even give you an extra bonus for—for being decent.'

He got up abruptly and walked over to the window to look out at the driving rain. The view of his back and the set of his shoulders was discouraging, and she wondered if, once again, she had said the wrong thing. Apparently she had, for he spoke with sudden anger.

'I may be short of money in your view, but I don't require paying for behaving with decency,' he said.

'Joss, I didn't mean—oh dear, I must be rather clumsy!' she said helplessly.

'You are a little,' he replied dispassionately, and turned round to face her. 'Your good intentions have come too late, I'm afraid, my dear. The will is already signed.'

She stared at him speechlessly, her fingers plucking nervously at the sheet.

'But it can't be,' she said then. 'You've only just finished lunch.'

'Over an hour ago. The lawyer chap wanted to get back to town and Sir Harry wanted his afternoon nap. They didn't waste time on formalities.'

'Were you present?'

'Yes.'

'So you know what was in the will?' He nodded.

'Oh hell, oh *hell*! What shall I do now?' she muttered feebly, and burrowed down in the pillows.

He came slowly back to stand beside the bed. She looked small and defeated and rather like a repentant little girl, with the pillow meeting uncomfortably in two pointed ears above her head. She gazed up at him in mute apology for hurting his feelings in the first place, and for having involved him in an impossible situation in the second.

'I'm sorry,' she whispered. 'I'm so very sorry to have

landed us all in such a mess.'

He sat down again on the bed, and the anger seemed to have left him.

'There's an obvious way out, you know,' he said. 'I'm surprised your formidable ingenuity hasn't already grasped it.'

'What do you mean?'

'Well, if we legitimized the story there would be no need for all this soul-searching and remorse.'

The room was growing dark and it was not easy to read his face. She struggled up against her pillows, blinking furiously.

'You mean get married—*really* get married?' she asked slowly.

'It's one way out, isn't it?'

'Easy living?' she said, on the defensive again because he had thoroughly disconcerted her, and his mouth twitched at the corners.

'You may, of course, think the suggestion springs largely from a desire to cash in on a good thing and settle down, but I happen to be quite fond of you, too,' he replied equably.

She did not know how to answer. She only knew that her own resistance had weakened so frightfully that last night she could have agreed; but now it was too late. The tears hung for a moment on her lashes and she said unhappily:

'Why couldn't you have asked me yesterday?'

He looked surprised.

'Would yesterday have made any difference to your answer?'

'Yes—yes, it would. You didn't know then about the will.'

'Oh, I see. Well, Christy, the will may not be worded quite as you expect. You had better accept my offer in the spirit in which it was meant.'

She frowned. 'You mean he hasn't left me Fairmile, after

156

all? He hasn't—he hasn't left it to *Brown*, has he?'

He smoothed down the corners of the pillows, adjusting their position to make her more comfortable.

'You'll have to ask the old man that. It's not my place to give away secrets, is it?' he asked, and she retorted, with an echo of her old, more hostile self:

'It's hardly a secret if you, a stranger, know it already.'

'And how long am I to remain a stranger?' he asked indulgently. 'Until you've grown up a little more?'

'I'm not a child.'

'No, you're not, but you frequently behave like one.'

'If you still think of me as a spoilt brat, why do you want to marry me?'

'I didn't say I wanted to. I simply offered the suggestion as a way out of the mess. Most likely it would be merely a matter of out of the frying pan into the fire.'

'For me?'

'More probably for me. You might, I fancy, turn out to be a bit of a shrew.'

'Oh!' she exclaimed wrathfully, resisting the unexpected temptation to wheedle a more tender avowal from him. 'And you, I suppose, fancy yourself as a sort of backwoods Petruchio! I've a good mind to pay you out by accepting you!'

'And accompany me to my rough shack with no amenities and the temperature often below zero?'

'There's no need to laugh at me,' she said crossly, and he gave a little sigh of impatience.

'Oh, Christy, how often have I told you to learn to laugh at yourself?' he said, and she felt confused and uncertain and suddenly humble.

'I—I wouldn't mind roughing things with—with someone I loved,' she told him shyly. 'I wish I understood you, Joss.'

'You will when you know me better,' he replied kindly. 'Now, would it cheer you up to see what I really bought you that day in London?'

Her head was beginning to ache again and she had difficulty in following him.

'This was your present—this thing Brown chose,' she said, pulling distastefully at the strings of her bed-jacket.

'Your disappointment was very evident! I will confess our Rose didn't show much imagination.'

'Or perhaps too much,' she countered shrewdly, and his eyebrows rose.

'Could be,' he said laconically, and got up and went into his room next door. He returned almost at once, tossing a small package into her lap, and stood, watching the wave of colour wash over her face as she opened it.

Whatever she had expected it was certainly not the fine single sapphire stone which winked up at her from a small jeweller's box. She took the ring out speechlessly and slipped it over her finger next to her wedding ring. It fitted perfectly.

'Nurse Brown certainly didn't choose that,' Joss observed, and suddenly sounded a little shy himself. 'I've been waiting for a suitable moment to produce the engagement ring we both forgot.'

'But, Joss, there was no need. It—it must have cost a fortune!' she stammered. 'How were you able——'

'No, it didn't come out of your two-fifty,' he said, 'neither did I pinch it.'

She looked up at him not knowing what to say, and the tears filled her eyes. This totally unexpected gesture seemed only a fitting climax to the whole incongruous day.

'Were you—were you already thinking about marriage when you bought it, then?' she asked.

'It had crossed my mind.'

'Then you were serious just now?'

'Perfectly. Think it over, won't you? The idea has its points, you know, and would save a whole lot of tiresome explanations.'

158

'No more than that?' she asked wistfully, and saw him hesitate.

'No more than that at present. You must learn to trust me as well as to know me, Christy,' he said then, and stooped to kiss her.

It would, of course, she thought disgustedly, have to be the very moment when Rose Brown saw fit to put her head in at the door to inquire how the invalid was.

'Oh, I beg your pardon,' she said with an exaggerated cough of embarrassment. 'I didn't realize you were here, Mr. Tavener. I'll go.'

But it was Joss who went, exchanging an enigmatical look with the nurse, and the other woman's taunts and hints of the day before crowded back upon Christy.

'My goodness!' Brown exclaimed, her eyes on the ring. 'Dear Joss *has* been spreading himself! I wonder where he finds the money—or perhaps you bought it yourself to bolster up your story.'

'If you've simply come to be unpleasant, I wish you'd go. My head aches,' said Christy wearily, and thrust her hand with the ring under the bedclothes.

'I've no wish to be unpleasant,' the nurse replied severely. 'I wouldn't like to think, though, that you were being taken in. He won't marry you.'

'And will my grandfather marry *you*, or have you hopes of Joss yourself?' snapped Christy, and Brown's long lashes fluttered demurely on her cheeks.

'Oh, I can't afford the luxury of turning down a certain future for an uncertain romance; but it's possible to have the best of both worlds, if one's clever,' she said. 'You look flushed, my dear. I'll go and get my thermometer.'

'You can take your damn thermometer and——' shouted Christy, but Brown's soft laugh drowned the rest of the sentence.

'Really, Christy, I don't know where you learn such expressions,' she said, and left the room.

CHAPTER EIGHT

THE bad weather continued for several days and, although up and about again, Christy was forced to remain in the house to avoid another chill.

The inactivity began to get on her nerves. Brown had a habit of suddenly appearing, her footsteps deadened by the rubber soles she wore about the house, giving no warning of approach. Christy, on the other hand, took great trouble to clatter through the empty rooms, nervously apprehensive of catching Joss and the nurse in a compromising situation, for it was plain they were all affected by the weather, and Joss himself appeared bored.

It was a relief to everyone when the rain finally stopped and Sir Harry could get out again in his chair, but to Christy there was a sudden sadness over the land. The gale had nearly stripped the trees and everywhere underfoot there was a sodden mass of rotting vegetation, enormous puddles and the damp smell of decay.

'The grounds really *are* in rather a dreadful state. Do you never have repairs done, Gramp?' she said, walking beside his chair while Joss pushed it.

'It would cost a mint to put this place right,' he barked crossly. 'Why should I care? I'm at the end of my days.'

'How do you know you are? Aren't you proud of Fairmile any longer?'

'Proud, proud! Pride has been my downfall in the past, and if you're not careful it'll be yours, too.'

'I'm not proud, Gramp,' she said, dancing a few steps on the wet grass, but he replied with sudden weariness:

'Oh yes, you are—you're not my granddaughter for nothing, young woman. You're just the sort to cut off your nose to spite your face.'

She walked soberly again and sent Joss a wary look, reminded of the snatch of song he so often whistled.

'Has *he* been putting you up to something?' she asked.

'Who, for heaven's sake? Talk sense!'

'Joss, of course.'

'I wouldn't dream of putting Sir Harry up to anything. He knows you better than I do,' Joss replied with a faint twinkle, and the old man gave a chuckle, mysteriously, restored to good humour.

'Silly young idiot, aren't you?' he said, addressing his granddaughter. 'You remember what I said. Don't cut off your nose to spite your face.'

'What did he mean about cutting off my nose?' she asked Joss uneasily, when they were alone together in the house.

'A timely warning, perhaps, that pride goes before a fall.'

'Now you're doing it, too—talking in riddles.'

'Not really riddles. Have you thought any more about marrying me?'

'No,' she said untruthfully, and wondered why he had brought the subject up now.

'Pity,' he said absently. 'Don't delay too long.'

'Why not? It can't make any difference. Gramp *is* up to something and I bet you're at the bottom of it! I'll go and ask him now.'

'Better not. He's having a private session with Rose, I think.'

'Is he asking her to marry him at last?' she jeered with an effort at flippancy which she was far from feeling. 'Well, that'll be a weight off her mind!'

Brown had indeed been summoned to the study and told to shut the door, and at Sir Harry's opening remarks, she settled in a chair with a little sigh of satisfaction.

'I've been wanting to have a talk with you, my dear, about your future,' he said. 'You've been very patient with a cantankerous old man, and I'd like you to know you haven't been forgotten in my will.'

'That's very generous of you, Sir Harry,' she murmured, her lashes demurely cast down. 'But I think you know very well that our relationship—mine at any rate—has been a little more than that of patient and nurse.'

'Has it, b'jove!' He gave a rather coarse chuckle. 'Well, if I'd been a whole man that might have been true, old though I am. You're an attractive wench, Rose, when you forget your prunes and prisms.'

'I'm past the age when I want gadding and romance. I'm very happy in the companionship of a mature mind. I'm a woman who could be content with that and nothing more—in certain circumstances,' she said, thinking with well-disguised exasperation that she couldn't give the old fool a plainer opening.

'Don't you believe it!' he scoffed, then suddenly bent a piercing regard on her.

'You'd have married me, wouldn't you?' he said, and continued before she could answer. 'And at one time I'd have asked you, but not now. It wouldn't do.'

'Why not?' she asked softly, aware that he might, for all his arrogance, need assurance that he still had something to offer a woman.

'Because my dear, I don't think you'd care to be nominal mistress of Fairmile if Joss and Christy are going to make their home here. She'd always take precedence, you know.'

She felt herself flushing, that rare, hard blush that was not becoming to her.

'But they are going back to Canada, surely,' she said, trying to speak with polite surprise.

'I think not. Joss always intended settling in England, he tells me. He has some good notions about the running of this place, too. I must confess it's a weight off my mind.'

She restrained herself with an effort from hurling the truth at him and watching that arrogant complacence dwindle like a pricked balloon, but the time was not yet. Her wits were sharper than Christy's, and Joss, she thought, could be easily dealt with once he knew his masquerade was no longer a secret.

'Mr. Tavener, of course, would naturally be co-operative over any plans you might have for Fairmile, Sir Harry,' she said a little dryly. 'He was, after all, rather fortunate in securing a prospective heiress for his—er—wife.'

He gave her a long, reflective look and sighed a little inexplicably.

'You've had your eye on him, haven't you?' he said, unexpectedly, and she half rose from her chair in protest.

'Sit down, sit down!' he said testily. 'I don't altogether blame you. It's been dull for you here. I'm a man of the world, my dear, and never did put too much importance on a little illicit amusement. You and Joss are two mature adults who know what you're about, but little Christy isn't, and I want this marriage to have a reasonable chance. She wouldn't be wise enough to shut her eyes to her husband's philandering, however innocent, and I don't want her hurt. She doesn't understand him at all at the moment, and she's only just begun to realize she's in love with him.'

'And don't you consider it's important that he should be in love with her?'

'Yes . . . yes . . . but it doesn't matter quite so much.'

'Joss evidently shares your view, since, contrary to your not very flattering suggestion, it was he who made the running with me,' she said waspishly, and he sighed again.

'Now don't take my observations amiss,' he said, sounding suddenly tired. 'But you must see for yourself that the present arrangement just wouldn't do. You're a young woman still. You might like to see a bit more of the world.'

'Are you giving me notice, Sir Harry?' she asked, still in a carefully controlled voice.

'Nothing definite, of course,' he replied vaguely. 'Just a hint that in your own good time——' He left the rest of his sentence in mid-air, and his beard brushed his waistcoat as his head fell forward in a surreptitious little snatch of sleep.

'And supposing their plans change?' she asked gently. 'Young people do tend to make sudden alterations in the early days. Wouldn't you need me then, Sir Harry?'

He shut his eyes, seeming already indifferent to the issue.

'Certainly I should need you—or someone like you,' he replied. 'Now go away like a good girl and let me sleep.'

She sat for a moment, longing to scream out the truth at him, to have him grateful in that moment of revelation, that she should stop on as his wife, but her professional instinct was still too strong to administer a deliberate shock. There must be other ways. She slipped out of the room without saying anything further, and went to find Christy.

It was not, however, until late afternoon that she had a chance of getting the girl alone. By then her anxiety had mounted to such a pitch that she was unable to lead up to the interview by the devious ways she had employed before. On meeting Christy in the corridor outside her room, she whisked her inside the door with scant excuse and began without preamble:

'I think it's time we had a showdown, Christy.'

'What, again?' asked Christy wearily, her thoughts still on her last little talk with Joss.

'I thought you would be sensible, since you've so much to lose,' Brown said. 'What did you want to go bleating to your grandfather for? I thought I'd made it clear that I would keep your secret if you kept mine.'

'I've told him nothing,' Christy said. 'What do you mean?'

'Well, Joss scarcely would have in the circumstances. Oh no, my dear, I'm afraid you've been dropping sly little hints about Joss and me. Making your home here, too! Did you put Joss up to that?'

'I don't know what you mean.'

'Don't you? Wasn't it your idea of putting a spoke in my wheel? Your grandfather would have married me once you were out of the way.'

164

Christy pushed the hair back from her forehead and looked with an absent sense of compassion at the nurse.

'Why do you make it out my fault?' she asked. 'Have you made it clear to him you were willing, Brownie?'

'Clear enough! But you had to go suggesting there was something between me and Joss.'

'I suggested nothing. Gramp, I suppose, could see for himself that you'd both—been amusing yourselves. What can *I* do about it?'

'You can get yourselves out of here,' Brown said crisply. 'Joss, of course, has been very clever in worming his way into the old man's regard—it wouldn't surprise me if he, too, hasn't some interest in the will. But whatever the true facts, I'll give you one more chance. Get out of here before I spill the beans. If you care so much for your grandfather's good opinion, save him the shock of knowing he's been deceived.'

Christy did not immediately answer. Her face in the fading light of late afternoon took on the delicate charm and slight disdain which had always annoyed the nurse.

'If Joss and I were really married, there'd be no need for any of this, would there?' she said gently, and Brown's controlled mouth curled in a rather cruel little smile.

'But you're not, my dear,' she replied silkily. 'And he's scarcely likely to oblige to save your face—unless there's something in it for him. It's time you got wise to yourself, Christy. We all have to learn lessons in love by experience —it's a pity you should have picked such uncompromising material for your first experiment. I don't want to be hard on you, my dear, but I have my own future to think of. You, with your youth and your little bit of money, can start again. Just get yourself and Joss out of here and leave me to pick up where I left off before you came.'

'I see,' said Christy, making absently for the door. 'I'll think about it.'

She thought about it for the rest of the day and far into

165

the night, her mind in a mild state of shock, but when morning came, with the long-delayed promise of a sunny day, she awoke and stretched her long young limbs in grateful salutation to the morning. Was not the unravelling of the tangle there for the taking? Had she not only to sink her pride a little and gamble on an off-chance?

She made a hearty breakfast, watched with a shade of puzzlement by Brown, who had been ready with soft condolences on a loss of appetite, and as she slipped past Joss's chair, bent down to whisper:

'Come to the drag in half an hour.'

'An assignation?' the nurse queried a little archly as the door slammed. 'The maze will be very damp after all that rain.'

'Very probably,' he replied, helping himself to more toast and marmalade. 'What are you up to now, dear Rose?'

She sat demurely behind the coffee pot and milk jug simmering on the copper hot-plate, and sent him a provocative glance.

'What are *you* up to, dear Joss?' she countered. 'I thought you and I understood one another.'

'Did you? But then it's never easy—or wise—to take a situation for granted, is it?' he said pleasantly, and got up and left the room.

He sauntered unhurriedly through the grounds and across the stable yard to the coach-house. He could see Christy's face with its flaxen curtain of hair, peering anxiously from a window of the drag, and smiled at the unconscious lapse into the habits of childhood.

'Come in—come in,' she said, opening a door and, as the familiar smell of must and mice greeted him when he climbed inside, he knew, with tenderness, that for a moment he shared with her that half-forgotten childhood and the importance of secrets revealed in a special hiding place.

'What is it?' he asked, and felt her shrink a little nervously into her corner of the drag.

'Joss—how long does it take to get married?' she asked somewhat breathlessly, and he turned to look at her.

'With a special licence, almost at once,' he replied. 'Why?'

'Could you get one? Does it cost an awful lot?'

'Are you in a hurry to get married, then?'

'Yes—yes, I am—before I have time to think about it, I mean. You see, Brown says——'

The story came tumbling out, with hasty but tactful omissions as to the personal relations between Joss and the nurse, Brown's knowledge of the truth, her threats to divulge it to Sir Harry, the dire necessity to nail the lie, if possible, and tie the nurse's hands.

'Dear me!' said Joss, when she had finished her rather incoherent explanation. 'You are a glutton for burning your boats, aren't you? You jump precipitately into a pretended marriage to get yourself out of a mess, and are apparently anxious to leap without thought into the real thing.'

'Not without thought—and you did ask me,' she said.

'So I did. But you won't be able to get out of this one so easily. I share your grandfather's views, you know, and don't hold with divorce. Is this your final bid to secure Fairmile?'

'No,' she said coldly. 'You know quite well I was ready to give up Fairmile that day Mr. Fellows came, but I was too late. I've—I've grown very fond of Gramp. I wouldn't like him to know about this deception.'

'And is that your only reason for being willing to throw in your lot with a stranger?'

She had tucked her feet under her, curling up on the dusty cushions as far away from him as she could get, but now she stretched out a tentative hand to touch him.

'No,' she said honestly. 'I—I have rather fallen for you, I'm afraid, Joss. I don't want to embarrass you, but I—I don't want you to go out of my life. It would be one in the eye for Brown, too.'

He caught the hand she was already withdrawing, and held it firmly in his own warm grasp.

'A curious combination of reasons,' he said, and she thought she detected laughter in his voice. 'Tell me, have you been imagining I've been having an affair with our Rose?'

'I heard you in the maze,' she said.

'I know.'

'You knew?' she exclaimed, sounding startled. 'Don't think I blame you, Joss,' she hurried on, striving for adult tolerance. 'After all, she's quite attractive when she's all dolled up and she's more of an age with you than I am. One must be civilized about these things, mustn't one? Sneaky little bitch!' she added, spoiling the whole thing, and then he did laugh.

'You're very refreshing,' he said. 'Would you believe me if I told you—not very gallantly—that our Rose was making a pass at me in the maze, not I at her?'

She moved towards him happily, rubbing her cheek against his shoulder.

'Of course—how very silly of me,' she said on such a long sigh of trust and relief that he smiled a little sadly.

'Keep your illusions as long as you can, my child,' he said. 'There's too little trust in the world—too many misunderstandings.'

'I suppose so. Did Brown try a bit of blackmail on you, too?'

'Oh yes—but she found me a tougher proposition than you, my poor sweet. Well, do you still want to get married?'

'Yes,' she said. 'If what Brown said was true and you really told Gramp you wanted to make your home here, we'd better, hadn't we? How do we set about it?'

His fingers twined in her hair.

'Such soft hair—like candy-floss,' he murmured.

'You said that when we first met. You must have liked

me a little, mustn't you?' she said. 'How do we set about getting married?'

'I've had a special licence for some days,' he informed her unexpectedly. 'There's nothing to stop us going off to the nearest registrar's office today.'

She drew away from him abruptly, the old antagonism returning, despite herself.

'You were banking on a certainty, then!' she exclaimed, sounding a little outraged, but he slipped a restraining arm round her shoulders.

'No, my darling—just on a profound hope,' he replied. 'You were always unpredictable and I took a chance.'

'You called me my darling as if you meant it,' she said slowly.

'And why wouldn't I?'

'I don't know, except that endearments were part of the game and meant nothing.'

'But perhaps it isn't a game any longer. Are you taking me on trust at last, Christy?'

'Yes, Joss,' she said simply, and asked herself, as he kissed her, what else there was for her to do but take him on trust. She did not expect him to tell her then that he loved her, for perhaps he did not, but he had shown fondness for her, and tenderness, and if he was simply making sure of an easy future she no longer cared. She only knew that she was ready to throw in her lot with his.

'Well,' he said, 'I'd better get on the telephone and clinch the arrangements. Can you be ready after lunch?'

'Y-yes,' she faltered, looking considerably startled.

'Good. Let's get out of here, then—this old barouche stinks like a sewer!'

Christy did not feel married at all when they returned from the little market town where the ceremony had been performed with such meaningless speed. The Registrar had been a brusque, dyspeptic-looking little man, his office bare

169

and rather dusty, and the two strange witnesses, procured hastily from nearby premises, uttered trite and mechanized clichés in the form of good wishes as if they were well accustomed to this demand on their services.

'It was all rather awful—kind of shoddy, wasn't it?' she said to Joss as they drove home, and he put a reassuring hand on her knee for a moment.

'Not in the best romantic tradition, certainly, but legal and binding, all the same. Don't forget that, will you?' he replied.

'No,' she said, and glanced a little dubiously at the familiar dark profile. She was really committed now, she thought uneasily, no game of pretence any longer but a reality bound by law. He was now her husband in fact, and she still knew nothing about him. 'Give me a cigarette, please.'

'Feeling cheated?' he asked, passing her his case. 'Regretting the frills and fuss of a white wedding—brides-maids, champagne, confetti and the bride looking radiant?'

'No,' she said, not liking the mockery underlying his words. 'I don't associate you with that kind of thing at all.'

'Perhaps the regrets should be mine, then. You would have made a delightful bride in the conventional tradition,' he replied unexpectedly. 'We can still have the champagne, though, and drink to your health. I'll have a word with your grandpapa.'

'Tell him, you mean?'

'Tell him what?'

'The truth, I suppose.'

'Maybe ... maybe ... but truth itself is so deceptive, isn't it?' he said ambiguously. She had no answer to such an enigmatic statement, so puffed at her cigarette in silence.

Back at Fairmile, the sensation of strangeness passed. Sir Harry, defeated by his crossword puzzle, irritably demanded help from everyone. Rose Brown presided demurely, as usual, over the tea-table, and Mrs. Heap had toasted the first crumpets of the season. It was impossible, Christy thought, to believe that things were any different, but later, when she went to her room to change for dinner, she was not so sure. Joss left their communicating door open and wandered in and out without embarrassment while she was dressing and, when she told him a little coolly that she was accustomed to privacy in her bedroom, observed conversationally:

'You'll have to get used to seeing me here, darling, I'm afraid. A husband has rights, you know.'

'Husband?'

'Yes. Had you forgotten already?'

'No, I hadn't forgotten,' she answered. 'But we've played at this for so long that——'

'It's hard to realize it's the real thing, isn't it?'

'I suppose so.' She did not add that the made it no easier for her to appreciate their change in relationship by being exactly as she had always known him, but he probably did not care for her in any deeper sense, and the demonstrative assurance of affection which she needed did not occur to him.

'Joss,' she said on a brave note of indifference, 'I owe you two hundred and fifty pounds. I'll write you a cheque now.'

She jumped up and began rummaging in her handbag for her cheque-book, conscious that he had not moved from the door.

'I should have thought that was cancelled,' he said.

'Oh no. Our contract only ended today—and you were most insistent that you were doing overtime,' she replied, and began to make out a cheque.

He stood watching her with lazy attention. In her skimpy slip with her pale hair bobbing on her bare shoulders, she looked like a little girl again, a little girl determined to present her governess with the finished exercise.

'There—now we're square,' she said, holding out the

cheque to him.

'I'm supposed to support you from now on,' he reminded her gently, and she saw his mouth tighten as she snapped back without thought.

'Can you?'

'That was a legitimate crack in the circumstances, I suppose,' he said. 'You think I've married you for your money and prospects, don't you?'

She stood there looking up at him a little helplessly, twisting the cheque between nervous fingers. She had hurt him in some unexpected fashion, she could see, but he had no right to be hurt. Had she not married him, careless of the motives Brown had attributed to him? Did he not know that this final precipitate act of hers sprang only from the fact that she wanted him and no longer cared whether he was a fortune-hunter or not?

'I don't know—I don't think I mind any more,' she stammered. 'I'm sorry if I hurt you, Joss, but you—you aren't making things very easy. Please—accept my cheque. I owe it to you, anyway.'

'For services rendered?' he asked, his mouth twisting in a wry little smile.

'Yes, of course—but—think of it as a wedding present if you'd rather,' she replied, and he took the piece of paper from her, placing it in his breast pocket without glancing at it and laid his hands lightly on her bare shoulders.

'And don't you expect a wedding present?' he asked, and as she shook her head without replying, he stooped and kissed her lightly on the forehead.

'Dear Christy,' he said. 'Thank you for your present, but it isn't this cheque, you know.'

'Not? What then?'

'Your blind trust in the end. That's rather precious to me, you know.'

'Joss . . .' she said, lifting up her face. 'Do you—do you care a tiny bit?'

172

'Don't you know?' he murmured quizzically, and was about to kiss her again when there was a knock on the door.

'Damn!' he exclaimed, letting her go, and Rose Brown came into the room without waiting for permission to enter.

'I beg your pardon,' she said with mock apology, but her eyes were bitter as she saw the state of Christy's undress and she made no effort to retire.

'I see,' she said with surprising directness, 'that my suggestion that you both made good use of your adjoining rooms wasn't necessary. How long has this been going on?'

'Are you out of your mind, Brown?' Christy exclaimed. Something other than finding them together had clearly upset the nurse in the first place, but surely she was not going to renew their private, rather nasty little feud in front of Joss.

'Now listen,' Brown said, her eyes feverish. 'I've just had a little altercation with Sir Harry in which he made some rather unpleasant suggestions. There's still time for me to woo him back to his old state of mind if you two will get out. Christy, I've given you rope enough—if you don't make it plain to your grandfather tonight that you have other plans for the future and intend leaving by the end of the week, I shall be forced to tell him the truth.'

'More blackmail?' said Christy coldly. 'You're a little late, Brown. We were married this afternoon.'

As she spoke she sent Joss a swift look for support, but he had gone back to the door between their rooms and merely propped himself there, his hands in his pockets, watching them both.

For a moment the nurse faltered, then her head went up and two spots of colour appeared on her cheeks.

'I don't believe it!' she said. 'Just another last-minute invention to put me off the scent. Well, I'm not so gullible —and even if it were true, do you imagine Sir Harry is going to feel any happier because he was tricked into changing his will?'

'I don't,' replied Christy wearily, 'even know what's in the will.'

'But Joss does. He was there.'

'You have to have witnesses for a will and Joss was the newest comer to the house. Do stop working yourself into the role of the dispossessed heroine. Gramp's left you something or you'd have been called as witness yourself.'

'I know very well I've been left something, but that's scarcely all I want,' the nurse spat back.

'I know. You want to be Lady Tavener. Well, I'm afraid I can't help you there, even if I wanted to,' said Christy, wondering why on earth Joss just stood there saying nothing.

'Oh yes, you can—by going away. I'll soon get the old gentleman back to where I had him before you came upsetting the apple-cart.'

Joss spoke at last.

'I think,' he said, his Canadian drawl rather pronounced, 'you can't be very well, Nurse Brown, or the old gentleman, as you refer to him, has upset you unduly. And I think my wife would like to finish dressing, if you don't mind.'

Brown wheeled round to face him. She really didn't look well, Christy thought uneasily, and there was no real telling what years of repression might do to an apparently well-balanced woman.

'Your wife!' Brown flung at him scornfully. 'Do you really expect me to believe that?'

'Would you like to see our marriage lines?' he inquired politely, but she did not trouble to accept a challenge which she took to be only a goad.

'I know your sort!' she went on with a reckless animation quite foreign to her. 'You'll cash in while the going's good, but show a clean pair of heels once you're caught out. I warned that stupid little ninny not to lose her heart to you, but of course she has, and I can't say it's going to break my heart to see her suffer in her first untimely essay into love.

Take her down a peg or two.'

There was a little silence. Christy felt the hot colour rush to her cheeks, but Joss did not look at her. He continued studying the nurse's contorted face with a thoughtful expression, and presently he said:

'Now that's very interesting. I was never sure—about Christy, you know—but hearing it from such an unfavourably biassed onlooker, I must believe it, mustn't I? Incidentally, you rather misled the poor girl on the score of our own relations, didn't you? Was that, perhaps, one of the unpleasant suggestions Sir Harry made to you just now? You will, of course, already have paved the way for a break-up by hinting that his grandson-in-law was not averse to your charms, but the old boy's shrewder than you think, you know. Now, will you please allow my wife to finish dressing?'

'Stop acting out this farce with me,' she cried furiously. 'You know very well I've been aware of the truth all along.'

'And bolstered up the lie in the first place when there was still time to come clean, because it suited your own ends,' he replied. 'We've all been playing games, it seems, but yours hasn't been very pretty, has it, Rose? Will you please go now? I'm quite capable of putting you outside the door, you know.'

She stood there looking at him blindly, then suddenly her whole demeanour altered with confusing unexpectedness.

'I'm sorry,' she said, 'I'm not well. I've been saying things I should have kept to myself. I'm not well. I shall excuse myself for dinner to Sir Harry.'

She turned and left the room, closing the door softly behind her, and Christy burst into tears.

'Hey, my poor darling, don't do that! You'll have a swollen face for Grandpa's celebration,' he chided, but he took her into his arms just the same and pressed the fair head against his shoulder.

'Poor B-Brownie ... do you think she's mad?' she sobbed.

'A little, perhaps. Personally, I suspect she's made a final assault on the old boy and been rejected in no unmeasured terms. She knows she's shot her bolt. This little exhibition was mostly spleen.'

'Poor Brownie...' she said again. 'I never knew she hated me because she wanted all the things I had—money, position, Fairmile—even you.'

'Well, it was you who got your man, wasn't it?' he said with laughter in his voice. 'Or perhaps it would be more accurate and certainly more gallant to say that it was I who won a long, hard battle. All those bickerings and slapping-downs!'

'It was mostly you who did the slapping down,' she complained, beginning to smile.

'Well, there were times when you needed it. You would never have fallen for a complacent lover—spoilt brat!'

'But you've never been a lover—mine, I mean,' she protested, her tears ceasing.

'Well, I've only just married you, so it's early to complain. Besides, I wanted to be sure.'

'Of yourself?'

'What do you think? I made up my own mind long before you made up yours.'

'*Did* you, Joss? Then——'

'Later,' he interrupted, giving her a little push across the room. 'We've wasted enough time as it is. Fix your face and get into that white thing I'm supposed to have chosen for you. Even if we didn't have wedding bells you'll have your white dress and champagne. Hurry up, now.'

When she was ready they went downstairs together. Sir Harry hailed them somewhat irritably and looked pointedly at the clock. The trolley stood at his elbow with the champagne and the Georgian glasses, and Christy was relieved to find that, true to her word, Rose Brown was absent.

'Come on, come on!' the old man barked impatiently. 'It can't take you all this time to get dolled up, Christy. H'm ... that white dress again, I see—most appropriate. What have you been doing to your eyes, monkey? Crying?'

'Certainly not! I got soap in them,' she replied, and saw her grandfather give Joss one of his blatant winks.

'What are you up to, Gramp?' she asked him suspiciously, bending over him to kiss him.

'What should I be up to?' he replied innocently. 'It's your good man who's up to something, if anyone is, demanding my best champagne and getting it, what's more. Come on, young feller—get the stuff open!'

The pop the cork made coming out of the bottle was a heartening sound, and as Christy watched the wine foam and scatter its myriad bubbles as it rose in the glasses, she felt her own spirits rise in unison.

This was her wedding day, however unreal it seemed. Joss watching her across the room, his glass held in readiness for a toast, was no longer the hired stranger chosen at random to play a part, and the lazy eyes which dwelt on her lingeringly were, perhaps, conveying the message she most wanted to hear.

She looked away. There had been time, hadn't there, before Brown burst in on them, even after she had gone? Perhaps she had read too much into his cryptic remarks; perhaps the nurse had been right when she had said he was only after her money.

'Brown not coming down?' she asked carelessly.

'No—got a pain in her belly or something,' her grandfather grunted. 'Badly adjusted female, that—not at all what I'd always thought her. Now, what's the toast to be? To the pair of you, I suppose. I shall have to drink it alone.' He raised his glass to them, then drained it at almost a swallow and helped himself to more.

'Sacrilegious—no palate, what?' he grinned. 'I needed a good pipe-opener—now I'll drink with proper respect to the wine.'

'And we must drink to you, Gramp, you old reprobate,' Christy said, toasting him in her turn, and his fierce blue eyes misted over.

'How like your mother you sounded then,' he said, and his voice sounded suddenly old. 'She's very like her altogether, Joss—same colouring, same small bones—but more spunk than poor Lisa—much more spunk. Gets that from me, of course. She'll make you a good wife yet if you have the patience, and I think you have. Here's to you both again, and hurry along with my first great-grandson. Too much time's been wasted—too much time . . .'

'You're not likely to get your great-grandson, Sir Harry, unless you're prepared to accept a bastard,' observed Rose Brown's voice from the doorway.

None of them had heard her come in. She stood there in a soft clinging dress which must have been new or put by for special occasions; jewels, or what passed for them, were in her ears, and her hair fell loosely about her smiling, composed face.

'I see you are all staring at me,' she said, still in that calm, measured voice. 'I can dress up, too, when it's an occasion, and for me, you see, this *is* an occasion. I must save you from yourself, Sir Harry, for you've been so beautifully taken in, poor dear.'

'Come in if you want a drink, but stop talking nonsense,' Sir Harry barked, and gestured to Joss to fill another glass.

'Oh, I'm not talking nonsense, Sir Harry. I will drink a toast, if that's what you want, but I think you should know the position,' Brown said, and, advancing into the room, took a glass from Joss and surveyed them all deliberately before taking a sip.

Christy, with a swift movement, had placed herself behind her grandfather's chair in readiness for the revelation she knew must come, but Joss merely propped himself

178

against the desk and appeared uninterested.

'You're not well, Brown. Drink your champagne and then go and lie down,' Sir Harry said, and Brown gave a little laugh.

'Not before I've said what I have to say,' she replied. 'What are you celebrating this time, Sir Harry?'

'My granddaughter's marriage, if you must know. Have you any objection?'

'Naturally not—but that, surely, was celebrated some time ago. Are they taking you for a ride again?'

'Brown...' said Christy pleadingly, 'please don't make trouble now.'

'Trouble? You're the one who's made the trouble, my dear—lying, pretending—all for your precious Fairmile!' Brown said. 'They're not married, Sir Harry—at least you should know that.'

Sir Harry swallowed the rest of his champagne at a gulp and held his glass out to Joss for a refill.

'On the contrary,' he said with remarkable self-control. 'They were married today—hence this little celebration. Perhaps you would like to drink to their happiness, Brown?'

Christy's startled gaze flew to Joss, but his own eyes remained fixed absently on a far corner of the room. He was, it seemed, indifferent to the terrible disclosures that the nurse was determined to make.

For a moment Brown faltered, her confidence shaken. Then she swallowed another mouthful of wine with indecent haste and said waspishly:

'Then don't you care that you've been deceived all this time? Don't you understand that the fact that they say they were married today is only another lie to get them out of a hole—or, at best, a rather necessary expedient to bolster up the first lie?'

To Christy it seemed like a nightmare. She twined her arms protectively round her grandfather's neck, and her soft hair brushed his cheek.

179

'Gramp,' she said, 'it's all true. I—I hired Joss to pretend because you'd got me in a corner—but later—well—it was all a silly game that I wanted to end long ago.'

He lifted an unsteady hand to touch her hair, then pushed her away a little impatiently.

'Do you think I didn't know?' he shouted suddenly. 'Do you think the chap you picked so casually had no sense of decency? I was aware of the whole blasted, idiotic set-up from the beginning. He told me.'

It would have been difficult to say which of the two women looked the more astonished, but of them both the nurse was the quicker to recover.

'Very clever!' she said, her feverish eyes on Joss. 'Put all your cards on the table and gamble on a bold move paying off. You told Sir Harry, too, I presume that your financial prospects could scarcely match Christy's?'

Joss did not reply, but the old man's beard bristled alarmingly as he raised his head.

'Oh, for God's sake, Brown! Joss could buy me up tomorrow twice over!' he exclaimed. 'Have you never heard of Cave's Bank of the Dominion of Canada? No, I suppose you wouldn't—it's an old-fashioned private concern, and has only just opened a branch in this country. Well, that's him.'

'You mean—he's a—a *banker*—respectable and sound and—and *bowler-hatted*!' Christy's voice sounded outraged, and at last Joss turned to look at her, his dark eyebrows lifting in the familiar, asymmetrical expression of amusement.

'Rather a let-down, isn't it?' he observed. 'No roughing it in the backwoods, no benighted shack, and a disgustingly healthy bank balance into the bargain. Poor Christy—I was playing a game too, you see.'

'*Oh!*' she exclaimed, and felt the tears trembling on her lashes. 'I might have *known* you'd turn out to be a fake! I—I should like to kick you—*hard!*'

His eyes dwelt on her tenderly, seeing, perhaps, the suscious brightness on her lashes and the nervous restlessness of her narrow hands, but he made no retort and a brief silence fell upon them all. Christy's eyes focused with difficulty on Brown and she wished the nurse would leave them; but Brown just stood there, and her own eyes seemed to be focussing badly.

'So all's well that ends well, that is it?' she said a little shrilly. 'The leisured classes sticking together, no matter what! I might have known! I might have known there was no place for me here. Do you think I cared about your damp, crumbling, archaic inheritance, Christy? Do you think, Joss, that I couldn't have got what I wanted from you if I'd really set my mind to it? And you, Sir Harry— would it have hurt you to lend me your name as a last gesture? Your time won't be long, you know, and when you've gone——'

'*Nurse Brown!*' Joss's voice cut across her speech hard and authoritative like a lash. She turned to look at him.

'It was Rose that evening in the maze, wasn't it?' she said. 'You threw my offer back in my face and then told Sir Harry that I tried to seduce you. Well, what if I did? I wanted position and a title, but I wanted a little more than the companionship of an old man who's past gratifying a woman's needs.'

'Brown!' warned Christy sharply, and at the same moment Sir Harry gave a little choking gasp and fell back in his chair.

'Gramp!' Christy cried, flinging herself on her knees beside him, and there was anguish in her voice. The old man was breathing stertorously, his hand to his heart, and Joss slid an arm round his shoulders, propping him up.

'Easy now, sir, easy,' he said quietly, then with silent swiftness, the nurse pushed them aside.

'Leave him to me,' she said, and became in a bewildering instant the cool, competent Rose Brown they had always known. Christy watched while the nurse went through the familiar motions of relieving her patient; pulse, medicine, the loosening of his collar, the quiet words of assurance. It seemed astonishing that she could become transformed so completely from the bitter, frustrated woman of a moment ago.

At last she straightened up and glanced a little enigmatically from Joss to Christy.

'He'll do,' she said. 'I won't embarrass you by my presence at dinner. I shall be leaving as soon as a replacement is found for me—a matter which I'm sure Mr.—er—Tavener already has in hand. Good night.'

'But, Brownie, won't you get him to bed—ring the doctor?' said Christy, helpless and confused. But the door had already closed behind the nurse, and Sir Harry cautiously opened an eye and winked.

'*Gramp*—you old humbug!' his granddaughter cried a little hysterically, tears from a mixture of relief and exasperation beginning to run down her cheeks. 'You were foxing again!'

'Best way to get rid of the termagant, wasn't it? Give me another glass of champagne,' he said.

Joss handed him a glass, but his face was grave.

'She's a sick woman,' he said. 'Try to think kindly of her, Sir Harry. She won't trouble you any more.'

'Oh, I don't grudge her efforts to become Lady Tavener,' the old man said. 'I was even willing to gratify her wish at one time. But I can't stomach the mischief she's made between you two. I was very blind, I suppose—very blind and rather presumptuous in my refusal to see.'

Christy slipped a hand through Joss's arm.

'You can't blame yourself, or even poor Brown,' she said gently. 'I was really the presumptuous one—stirring everyone up because I wanted Fairmile. Well, I don't any more, Gramp. I tried to stop you from changing your will, but I was too late. I don't want Fairmile.'

Her grandfather shot her a calculating look and cleared his throat.

'You don't get it, either. I've left it to your husband,' he said.

She caught her breath sharply and her eyes grew wide with surprise.

'To *Joss*!'

'In trust for your sons. Bless me, Christy! He's the only one of us who could afford to keep the place up—besides, he's got ideas about orphans. This bank of his endows kids' homes all over Canada. He wants to start 'em here as well.'

'Is *that* why you came over?' she asked Joss slowly, and he was not altogether sure he liked the look in her eyes.

'Well, that and getting the London branch of the Bank going.'

'But why couldn't you have told me?'

'My dear Christy,' he retorted with a little shrug, 'you were so plainly convinced that I was a ne'er-do-well in need of money, it seemed a shame to disillusion you. Besides——'

'Besides what?'

'Later,' he said with tantalizing finality, just as he had upstairs.

'Later ... later ... it's always later!' she muttered, and, for the first time, thought of the approaching night. Albeit with mockery, he had respected that keyless door between their two rooms, but now there was no need for forebearance, neither would she have the right to deny him.

She looked away from him hastily, remembering his awkward knack of reading her thoughts, and asked quietly:

'And the orphanage? Was that an invention, too?'

'Oh no,' he replied calmly. 'My origin's still obscure and I really *was* named after that dirty little creek in the backwoods. Old man Cave adopted me when I was seven—it

183

was his initials on my brushes, incidentally, Christy. He put me into the Bank in due course and left it to me when he died—nobody quite knew why, unless it sprang from his passion for endowing orphanages. I told you he was an eccentric—but the least I felt I could do in return for my good fortune was to carry on his life's work. Would you mind orphans enjoying the privileges of Fairmile?'

'No,' she said, sounding a little dazed. 'No—I don't think so.'

'Always said this place needed kids—lots of 'em!' Sir Harry chuckled.

Dinner was served as usual, and as usual coffee was brought to the study and later the accustomed nightcaps. Sir Harry seemed tired and took several surreptitious naps, and presently Tom came in to get him to bed.

It was the moment Christy had been dreading, for Joss, having been stripped of the disguise she herself had thrust upon him, seemed a stranger again. She had come to know him through misconception and the self-betrayal of her own heart; must she now start afresh and find that she had married a totally different person? He had been watching her for a long time and his voice broke softly into her troubled thoughts.

'Get to bed,' he said with gentleness. 'Tomorrow is another day...'

Upstairs in her room she poked the dying fire into life and squatted in front of it, feeling suddenly cold. The crowded events of the day had exhausted her, and the dingy Registrar's office, Brown's horrifying behaviour, Gramp's outrageous jest and Joss's unexpected revelations, jumbled together in her mind like a confused nightmare. She could think of Brown with compassion now, but of Joss she did not want to think at all, knowing that this time there would be no mock marriage, that she had forfeited her right to call the tune.

She did not know he had come up, so deep in contemplation was she, until she felt herself gently lifted to her feet.

'You may kick me now if you like. I won't retaliate with that spanking,' he said, and suddenly he was no longer a stranger. She clung to him a little desperately, seeking in herself the humility and charity that love must demand, the passionate desire to grow, in time, to his stature.

'Why, my darling,' he said with concern, 'do you mind so much about Fairmile?'

'I wasn't thinking of Fairmile,' she said. 'Just of you and—and how small you must have thought me. You've always seen the worst of me—the spoilt brat.'

'There have been other moments, too,' he told her gravely, 'moments I had to let go by because you weren't ready for me.'

'Will I have to begin all over again, Joss?' she asked, and he smiled.

'I don't think so. I'm still the same old Joss—tramp, lay-about—any unflattering thing you like to call me. I couldn't help playing up to your fixed conception of me, but I never really misled you.'

'No, I suppose you didn't. Did you—did you know I was falling in love with you?'

'I sincerely hoped you were.'

'But you never once said——'

'Yes?'

She fidgeted, suddenly uneasy.

'Well, I—I've been waiting for you to tell me *you* loved *me*.'

'I've been waiting for you to ask me.'

'One doesn't ask a man that sort of thing,' she said, trying to sound disdainful.

'Doesn't one? How old-fashioned! I haven't found you backward in coming forward over anything else you wanted to know. Why do you suppose I agreed in the first place to this ridiculous charade of yours?'

185

Oddly enough, it had not yet occurred to her to wonder.

'Why did you?' she asked, adding with a flash of her old spirit: 'Taking my money when you didn't need it—even letting me buy your beer in the pub!'

He released her long enough to delve in his breast pocket for his wallet. He took out her two cheques, carefully folded, and tore them across.

'I never cashed the first one, you see,' he said.

'Then why——'

'Well, the proposition was novel enough to be intriguing —also, I think, I wanted to teach you a lesson. You were so very sure of yourself, my dear, and so foolishly trusting.'

'And then?' she faltered, wanting an admission so much, but willing, now, to accept a deserved rebuff so long as he went on looking at her like that.

'And then, of course, I fell in love with you, as you ought to have guessed,' he replied with a certain asperity, and took her back into his arms. 'Oh, Christy, you were so blind, so ready always to think the worst of me. You know so little of the world, despite your boasting. Did you ever stop to consider what the consequences might have been had you really picked on a stranger who lived by his wits?'

'I suppose not,' she said, and inexplicably began to weep. 'I know so little of anything, Joss. Can you be patient with me?'

He gave her a little shake.

'What do you think I've been all these weeks?' he retorted. 'Anyway, you married me, still thinking the worst of me, and for that I must forgive you much, mustn't I? Do you grudge me Fairmile, darling? There was no arguing with your grandfather, you know.'

'I'm sure there wasn't. No—how can I grudge you anything now, Joss? I was so stingy with you in the first place, wasn't I? Fairmile was just a dream, anyway. What would I have done with all those empty rooms, and no one to share them with?

'We'll share it all together,' he said, his lips brushing her hair. 'And if some poor homeless little blighters can share it with us too, and, later, with our children, then the place will come alive again and fulfil a purpose in life. Can you look at it that way? That orphanage way back in Canada taught me a lot of things, my dearest, and now I've found you I can get on with living.'

'What a strange thing to say,' she replied wonderingly. 'You had everything, really—money, position and an unlimited choice of wives, I should have said.'

'Well, life plays you tricks, as you are beginning to find out,' he said, and his eyes were suddenly grave. 'The one thing I never had, Christy, was affection, and perhaps that's what I've always been seeking; affection, love, the only charity—remember? My benefactor hadn't learnt that, and the women who came my way sold themselves very charmingly and very readily for what they could get out of me. As to wives'—he finished on a lighter note—'well, maybe I've got my deserts after all these years!'

'Then that may pay you back for all the smug satisfaction you've had at my expense, Josiah Tavener!' she retorted, with the old resolve to have the last word, and his smile held an indulgent tenderness as he smacked her gently on the behind.

'Time will show,' he said. 'Christy, you once told me you thought I would make an excellent lover. Have you forgotten?'

'No.'

'And this is our wedding night. Have you forgotten that, too?'

'No,' she said again, her eyes on the door standing open between their rooms. 'No one ever did produce a key, did they?'

He let her go, running his hands along her bare shoulders and down the smooth, soft folds of the white dress. Then he

187

caught her fingers and brought them swiftly to his lips.

'A key won't be necessary any longer—nor a chair propped under the door knob,' he said. 'Get to bed, my love—it's growing late.'

Mills & Boon's Paperbacks

JUNE

HEALING IN THE HILLS by Ruth Clemence

It was in the Lake District that Ismay sought escape from the pain of one romantic experience—only to find another. But this time the situation was the other way round. With Peter, the love had been on his side. With Lewis, it seemed his interest in her was only as a nurse who could be useful to him. Her rival was his work . . .

DEVIL IN A SILVER ROOM by Violet Winspear

Margo Jones had loved Michel, although in the end he had married someone else. But she had never forgotten, and when five years later he died she found herself going to the French chateau of Satancourt to look after his son—and to cope with his inscrutable brother Paul.

GENTLE TYRANT by Lucy Gillen

Laurie couldn't help resenting the three McAdam brothers, who had bought her beloved home, but she had to admit that Russ, who had taken her on as his secretary, couldn't be nicer to work for, while Rod was an absolute charmer. It was the third brother, the tyrannical Quin, who presented the real problem!

A SONG BEGINS by Mary Burchell

Anthea had a talent—a singing voice too lovely to be hidden. But she was to find that, like a beautiful face, it can bring the owner good fortune, or real tragedy.

SIGH NO MORE by Elizabeth Ashton

'Men were deceivers ever,' Imogen told herself bitterly, after Raymond had let her down. She was never going to let it happen again. Her resolve might have weakened when she met Christian Wainwright and knew she could easily fall in love with him—but Christian had another love, with which Imogen couldn't possibly compete!

20p net each

Mills & Boon's Paperbacks
JUNE (contd.)

A KISS FROM SATAN by ANNE HAMPSON

'Place your hand on a woman's heart and she's yours instantly,' said the arrogant Greek Julius Spiridon. Gale, embittered after being let down by the man she loved, had vowed never to let a man touch her heart again. So she was absolutely determined to fight the attraction she so unwillingly felt for Julius . . .

LEGACY OF THE PAST by ANNE MATHER

The only two men in Madeline's life so far had been gentle and kind, wanting only to protect and cherish her. Nicholas Vitale was anything but gentle, kind or protective—but Madeline couldn't resist him. But if she got involved with him, would she bring herself anything but heart-break?

THREE FOR A WEDDING by BETTY NEELS

Phoebe Brook hadn't planned to take a nursing job in Holland, still less to pass herself off as her sister Sybil in the process—but the deed was done now. What would Doctor Lucius van Someren do when and if he found out about Phoebe's deception? And that was not the only problem to face Phoebe when she arrived in Holland.

WIND RIVER by MARGARET WAY

Perri had come here to Coorain, in the Dead Heart of Australia, to work, not to teeter on the brink of disaster with a man like the cattle baron Gray Faulkner. But how could she avoid it?

20p net each

FREE!

YOUR COPY OF OUR CATALOGUE
OF MILLS & BOON ROMANCES
NOW AVAILABLE

If you enjoyed this MILLS & BOON romance and would like a list of other MILLS & BOON romances available, you can receive a free Catalogue by completing the coupon below and posting it off today. This opportunity to read more MILLS & BOON romances should not be missed. Your free Catalogue will be posted off to you immediately.

Over the page are listed 50 selections from our current catalogue. This list may include titles you missed and have had difficulty in getting from your usual stockist. Tick your selection, fill in the coupon and send the whole page to us with your remittance. We'll do the rest. Happy reading!

MILLS & BOON READER SERVICE
PO BOX 236
14 SANDERSTEAD ROAD
CROYDON, SURREY CR2 0YG

Please send me the free Mills & Boon Romance Catalogue

Please send me the titles ticked*

*All Mills & Boon paperback titles ordered through the Mills & Boon Reader Service are 20p each. Note to cover postage and handling, will United Kingdom readers please add 2p per book. Overseas readers are asked to add 10p per book and use international money orders where possible.

I enclose £.. (no C.O.D.)

NAME .... Miss/Mrs

ADDRESS ....

....

Town .... County/Country ....

Postal Code MB573

HAVE YOU MISSED ANY OF THESE FAVOURITES?

PLEASE TICK YOUR REQUIREMENTS
TURN OVER FOR HANDY ORDER FORM